# THE ULTIMATE

# BOONDOCKER'S

★ *LOGBOOK* & *JOURNAL* ★

## DISPERSED CAMPING

# NOLA LEE KELSEY

# Soggy Nomad Press

Las Vegas, NV, USA

ISBN: 978-1-957532-35-6

Cover design by Nola Lee Kelsey

Start Date: _____ End Date: _____

Property of:

_____

_____

_____

Phone: _____

Email: _____

*If found, please return!*

"And into the forest I go,
to lose my mind and find my soul."

- John Muir

# Content

# MY CAMPSITES
# QUICK REFERENCE

| Date | State/Region | Campsite | Page # |
|------|--------------|----------|--------|
|      |              |          |        |
|      |              |          |        |
|      |              |          |        |
|      |              |          |        |
|      |              |          |        |
|      |              |          |        |
|      |              |          |        |
|      |              |          |        |
|      |              |          |        |
|      |              |          |        |
|      |              |          |        |
|      |              |          |        |
|      |              |          |        |
|      |              |          |        |
|      |              |          |        |
|      |              |          |        |
|      |              |          |        |
|      |              |          |        |
|      |              |          |        |
|      |              |          |        |
|      |              |          |        |
|      |              |          |        |

# MY CAMPSITES
# QUICK REFERENCE

| Date | State/Region | Campsite | Page # |
|------|--------------|----------|--------|
|      |              |          |        |
|      |              |          |        |
|      |              |          |        |
|      |              |          |        |
|      |              |          |        |
|      |              |          |        |
|      |              |          |        |
|      |              |          |        |
|      |              |          |        |
|      |              |          |        |
|      |              |          |        |
|      |              |          |        |
|      |              |          |        |
|      |              |          |        |
|      |              |          |        |
|      |              |          |        |
|      |              |          |        |
|      |              |          |        |
|      |              |          |        |
|      |              |          |        |

# MY CAMPSITES
# QUICK REFERENCE

| Date | State / Region | Campsite | Page # |
|------|----------------|----------|--------|
|      |                |          |        |
|      |                |          |        |
|      |                |          |        |
|      |                |          |        |
|      |                |          |        |
|      |                |          |        |
|      |                |          |        |
|      |                |          |        |
|      |                |          |        |
|      |                |          |        |
|      |                |          |        |
|      |                |          |        |
|      |                |          |        |
|      |                |          |        |
|      |                |          |        |
|      |                |          |        |
|      |                |          |        |
|      |                |          |        |
|      |                |          |        |
|      |                |          |        |
|      |                |          |        |

# MY CAMPSITES
# QUICK REFERENCE

| Date | State/ Region | Campsite | Page # |
|---|---|---|---|
| | | | |
| | | | |
| | | | |
| | | | |
| | | | |
| | | | |
| | | | |
| | | | |
| | | | |
| | | | |
| | | | |
| | | | |
| | | | |
| | | | |
| | | | |
| | | | |
| | | | |
| | | | |
| | | | |
| | | | |
| | | | |
| | | | |

# MY CAMPSITES
# QUICK REFERENCE

| Date | State/Region | Campsite | Page # |
|------|--------------|----------|--------|
|      |              |          |        |
|      |              |          |        |
|      |              |          |        |
|      |              |          |        |
|      |              |          |        |
|      |              |          |        |
|      |              |          |        |
|      |              |          |        |
|      |              |          |        |
|      |              |          |        |
|      |              |          |        |
|      |              |          |        |
|      |              |          |        |
|      |              |          |        |
|      |              |          |        |
|      |              |          |        |
|      |              |          |        |
|      |              |          |        |
|      |              |          |        |
|      |              |          |        |
|      |              |          |        |

# Campsite Dog Log

# CAMPSITE LOG

DATE(S): _____

CAMP: _____

LOCATION: _____

DIRECTIONS: _____

STATE: _____ ALTITUDE: _____ GPS: _____

ROAD CONDITIONS: _____

CELL SIGNAL: _____ WIFI: _____ WEBSITE: _____

WEATHER: _____ NOISE: _____ MAXIMUM STAY: _____

PROS: _____

CONS: _____

TIPS FOR NEXT STAY: _____

NOTES: _____

☆ ☆ ☆ ☆ ☆

## ON-SITE CAMP AMENITIES:

☐ Nature Reserve

☐ Picnic Tables          ☐ Fire Pit          ☐ Historic Sites

☐ Hiking Trails          ☐ Water             ☐ Fishing

☐ Boat Dock              ☐ Shade             ☐ OHV Trails

☐ Pit Toilet             ☐ Views             ☐ Other _____

## NEARBY AMENITIES & NECESSITIES:

GAS: _____  PROPANE: _____

GROCERIES: _____  C-STORE: _____

DRINKING WATER: _____  NON-POTABLE WATER: _____

DUMP STATION: _____  DUMPSTER: _____

LAUNDRY: _____  SHOWERS: _____

FIREWOOD: _____  DOG PARK: _____

HIKING TRAILS: _____

ATTRACTIONS: _____

RANGER STATION: _____

OTHER: _____

# IMAGES & JOURNAL NOTES

# CAMPSITE LOG

DATE(S): _____

CAMP: _____

LOCATION: _____

DIRECTIONS: _____

STATE: _____ ALTITUDE: _____ GPS: _____

ROAD CONDITIONS: _____

CELL SIGNAL: _____ WIFI: _____ WEBSITE: _____

WEATHER: _____ NOISE: _____ MAXIMUM STAY: _____

PROS: _____

CONS: _____

TIPS FOR NEXT STAY: _____

NOTES: _____

☆ ☆ ☆ ☆ ☆

## ON-SITE CAMP AMENITIES:

☐ Picnic Tables    ☐ Fire Pit    ☐ Nature Reserve
☐ Hiking Trails    ☐ Water    ☐ Historic Sites
☐ Boat Dock    ☐ Shade    ☐ Fishing
☐ Pit Toilet    ☐ Views    ☐ OHV Trails
                            ☐ Other _____

## NEARBY AMENITIES & NECESSITIES:

GAS: _____    PROPANE: _____

GROCERIES: _____    C-STORE: _____

DRINKING WATER: _____    NON-POTABLE WATER: _____

DUMP STATION: _____    DUMPSTER: _____

LAUNDRY: _____    SHOWERS: _____

FIREWOOD: _____    DOG PARK: _____

HIKING TRAILS: _____

ATTRACTIONS: _____

RANGER STATION: _____

OTHER: _____

# IMAGES & JOURNAL NOTES

# CAMPSITE LOG

DATE(S): _____

CAMP: _____

LOCATION: _____

DIRECTIONS: _____

STATE: _____ ALTITUDE: _____ GPS: _____

ROAD CONDITIONS: _____

CELL SIGNAL: _____ WIFI: _____ WEBSITE: _____

WEATHER: _____ NOISE: _____ MAXIMUM STAY: _____

PROS: _____

CONS: _____

TIPS FOR NEXT STAY: _____

NOTES: _____

☆ ☆ ☆ ☆ ☆

## ON-SITE CAMP AMENITIES:

- ☐ Picnic Tables
- ☐ Hiking Trails
- ☐ Boat Dock
- ☐ Pit Toilet

- ☐ Fire Pit
- ☐ Water
- ☐ Shade
- ☐ Views

- ☐ Nature Reserve
- ☐ Historic Sites
- ☐ Fishing
- ☐ OHV Trails
- ☐ Other _____

## NEARBY AMENITIES & NECESSITIES:

GAS: _____ PROPANE: _____

GROCERIES: _____ C-STORE: _____

DRINKING WATER: _____ NON-POTABLE WATER: _____

DUMP STATION: _____ DUMPSTER: _____

LAUNDRY: _____ SHOWERS: _____

FIREWOOD: _____ DOG PARK: _____

HIKING TRAILS: _____

ATTRACTIONS: _____

RANGER STATION: _____

OTHER: _____

# IMAGES & JOURNAL NOTES

# CAMPSITE LOG

DATE(S): _____

**CAMP:** _____

**LOCATION:** _____

**DIRECTIONS:** _____

**STATE:** _____ **ALTITUDE:** _____ **GPS:** _____

**ROAD CONDITIONS:** _____

**CELL SIGNAL:** _____ **WIFI:** _____ **WEBSITE:** _____

**WEATHER:** _____ **NOISE:** _____ **MAXIMUM STAY:** _____

**PROS:** _____

**CONS:** _____

**TIPS FOR NEXT STAY:** _____

**NOTES:** _____

☆ ☆ ☆ ☆ ☆

## ON-SITE CAMP AMENITIES:

- ☐ Picnic Tables
- ☐ Hiking Trails
- ☐ Boat Dock
- ☐ Pit Toilet
- ☐ Fire Pit
- ☐ Water
- ☐ Shade
- ☐ Views
- ☐ Nature Reserve
- ☐ Historic Sites
- ☐ Fishing
- ☐ OHV Trails
- ☐ Other _____

## NEARBY AMENITIES & NECESSITIES:

**GAS:** _____ **PROPANE:** _____

**GROCERIES:** _____ **C-STORE:** _____

**DRINKING WATER:** _____ **NON-POTABLE WATER:** _____

**DUMP STATION:** _____ **DUMPSTER:** _____

**LAUNDRY:** _____ **SHOWERS:** _____

**FIREWOOD:** _____ **DOG PARK:** _____

**HIKING TRAILS:** _____

**ATTRACTIONS:** _____

**RANGER STATION:** _____

**OTHER:** _____

# IMAGES & JOURNAL NOTES

# CAMPSITE LOG

DATE(S): _____

**CAMP:** _____

**LOCATION:** _____

**DIRECTIONS:** _____

**STATE:** _____ **ALTITUDE:** _____ **GPS:** _____

**ROAD CONDITIONS:** _____

**CELL SIGNAL:** _____ **WIFI:** _____ **WEBSITE:** _____

**WEATHER:** _____ **NOISE:** _____ **MAXIMUM STAY:** _____

**PROS:** _____

**CONS:** _____

**TIPS FOR NEXT STAY:** _____

**NOTES:** _____

☆ ☆ ☆ ☆ ☆

## ON-SITE CAMP AMENITIES:

- ☐ Picnic Tables
- ☐ Hiking Trails
- ☐ Boat Dock
- ☐ Pit Toilet
- ☐ Fire Pit
- ☐ Water
- ☐ Shade
- ☐ Views
- ☐ Nature Reserve
- ☐ Historic Sites
- ☐ Fishing
- ☐ OHV Trails
- ☐ Other _____

## NEARBY AMENITIES & NECESSITIES:

**GAS:** _____ **PROPANE:** _____

**GROCERIES:** _____ **C-STORE:** _____

**DRINKING WATER:** _____ **NON-POTABLE WATER:** _____

**DUMP STATION:** _____ **DUMPSTER:** _____

**LAUNDRY:** _____ **SHOWERS:** _____

**FIREWOOD:** _____ **DOG PARK:** _____

**HIKING TRAILS:** _____

**ATTRACTIONS:** _____

**RANGER STATION:** _____

**OTHER:** _____

# IMAGES & JOURNAL NOTES

# CAMPSITE LOG

DATE(S): _____

**CAMP:** _____

**LOCATION:** _____

**DIRECTIONS:** _____

**STATE:** _____ **ALTITUDE:** _____ **GPS:** _____

**ROAD CONDITIONS:** _____

**CELL SIGNAL:** _____ **WIFI:** _____ **WEBSITE:** _____

**WEATHER:** _____ **NOISE:** _____ **MAXIMUM STAY:** _____

**PROS:** _____

**CONS:** _____

**TIPS FOR NEXT STAY:** _____

**NOTES:** _____

☆ ☆ ☆ ☆ ☆

## ON-SITE CAMP AMENITIES:

- ☐ Picnic Tables
- ☐ Hiking Trails
- ☐ Boat Dock
- ☐ Pit Toilet
- ☐ Fire Pit
- ☐ Water
- ☐ Shade
- ☐ Views
- ☐ Nature Reserve
- ☐ Historic Sites
- ☐ Fishing
- ☐ OHV Trails
- ☐ Other _____

## NEARBY AMENITIES & NECESSITIES:

**GAS:** _____ **PROPANE:** _____

**GROCERIES:** _____ **C-STORE:** _____

**DRINKING WATER:** _____ **NON-POTABLE WATER:** _____

**DUMP STATION:** _____ **DUMPSTER:** _____

**LAUNDRY:** _____ **SHOWERS:** _____

**FIREWOOD:** _____ **DOG PARK:** _____

**HIKING TRAILS:** _____

**ATTRACTIONS:** _____

**RANGER STATION:** _____

**OTHER:** _____

# IMAGES & JOURNAL NOTES

# CAMPSITE LOG

DATE(S): _____

CAMP: _____

LOCATION: _____

DIRECTIONS: _____

STATE: _____ ALTITUDE: _____ GPS: _____

ROAD CONDITIONS: _____

CELL SIGNAL: _____ WIFI: _____ WEBSITE: _____

WEATHER: _____ NOISE: _____ MAXIMUM STAY: _____

PROS: _____

CONS: _____

TIPS FOR NEXT STAY: _____

NOTES: _____

☆ ☆ ☆ ☆ ☆

## ON-SITE CAMP AMENITIES:

- ☐ Picnic Tables
- ☐ Hiking Trails
- ☐ Boat Dock
- ☐ Pit Toilet
- ☐ Fire Pit
- ☐ Water
- ☐ Shade
- ☐ Views
- ☐ Nature Reserve
- ☐ Historic Sites
- ☐ Fishing
- ☐ OHV Trails
- ☐ Other _____

## NEARBY AMENITIES & NECESSITIES:

GAS: _____ PROPANE: _____

GROCERIES: _____ C-STORE: _____

DRINKING WATER: _____ NON-POTABLE WATER: _____

DUMP STATION: _____ DUMPSTER: _____

LAUNDRY: _____ SHOWERS: _____

FIREWOOD: _____ DOG PARK: _____

HIKING TRAILS: _____

ATTRACTIONS: _____

RANGER STATION: _____

OTHER: _____

# IMAGES & JOURNAL NOTES

# CAMPSITE LOG

DATE(S): _____

CAMP: _____

LOCATION: _____

DIRECTIONS: _____

STATE: _____ ALTITUDE: _____ GPS: _____

ROAD CONDITIONS: _____

CELL SIGNAL: _____ WIFI: _____ WEBSITE: _____

WEATHER: _____ NOISE: _____ MAXIMUM STAY: _____

PROS: _____

CONS: _____

TIPS FOR NEXT STAY: _____

NOTES: _____

☆ ☆ ☆ ☆ ☆

## ON-SITE CAMP AMENITIES:

- ☐ Picnic Tables
- ☐ Hiking Trails
- ☐ Boat Dock
- ☐ Pit Toilet

- ☐ Fire Pit
- ☐ Water
- ☐ Shade
- ☐ Views

- ☐ Nature Reserve
- ☐ Historic Sites
- ☐ Fishing
- ☐ OHV Trails
- ☐ Other _____

## NEARBY AMENITIES & NECESSITIES:

GAS: _____  PROPANE: _____

GROCERIES: _____  C-STORE: _____

DRINKING WATER: _____  NON-POTABLE WATER: _____

DUMP STATION: _____  DUMPSTER: _____

LAUNDRY: _____  SHOWERS: _____

FIREWOOD: _____  DOG PARK: _____

HIKING TRAILS: _____

ATTRACTIONS: _____

RANGER STATION: _____

OTHER: _____

# IMAGES & JOURNAL NOTES

_____
_____
_____
_____
_____
_____
_____
_____
_____
_____
_____
_____
_____
_____
_____

# CAMPSITE LOG

DATE(S): _____

**CAMP:** _____

**LOCATION:** _____

**DIRECTIONS:** _____

**STATE:** _____ **ALTITUDE:** _____ **GPS:** _____

**ROAD CONDITIONS:** _____

**CELL SIGNAL:** _____ **WIFI:** _____ **WEBSITE:** _____

**WEATHER:** _____ **NOISE:** _____ **MAXIMUM STAY:** _____

**PROS:** _____

**CONS:** _____

**TIPS FOR NEXT STAY:** _____

**NOTES:** _____

☆ ☆ ☆ ☆ ☆

## ON-SITE CAMP AMENITIES:

☐ Picnic Tables    ☐ Fire Pit    ☐ Nature Reserve
☐ Hiking Trails    ☐ Water    ☐ Historic Sites
☐ Boat Dock    ☐ Shade    ☐ Fishing
☐ Pit Toilet    ☐ Views    ☐ OHV Trails
   ☐ Other _____

## NEARBY AMENITIES & NECESSITIES:

**GAS:** _____ **PROPANE:** _____

**GROCERIES:** _____ **C-STORE:** _____

**DRINKING WATER:** _____ **NON-POTABLE WATER:** _____

**DUMP STATION:** _____ **DUMPSTER:** _____

**LAUNDRY:** _____ **SHOWERS:** _____

**FIREWOOD:** _____ **DOG PARK:** _____

**HIKING TRAILS:** _____

**ATTRACTIONS:** _____

**RANGER STATION:** _____

**OTHER:** _____

# IMAGES & JOURNAL NOTES

# CAMPSITE LOG

DATE(S): _____

CAMP: _____

LOCATION: _____

DIRECTIONS: _____

STATE: _____ ALTITUDE: _____ GPS: _____

ROAD CONDITIONS: _____

CELL SIGNAL: _____ WIFI: _____ WEBSITE: _____

WEATHER: _____ NOISE: _____ MAXIMUM STAY: _____

PROS: _____

CONS: _____

TIPS FOR NEXT STAY: _____

NOTES: _____

_____

☆ ☆ ☆ ☆ ☆

## ON-SITE CAMP AMENITIES:

- ☐ Picnic Tables
- ☐ Hiking Trails
- ☐ Boat Dock
- ☐ Pit Toilet

- ☐ Fire Pit
- ☐ Water
- ☐ Shade
- ☐ Views

- ☐ Nature Reserve
- ☐ Historic Sites
- ☐ Fishing
- ☐ OHV Trails
- ☐ Other _____

## NEARBY AMENITIES & NECESSITIES:

GAS: _____ PROPANE: _____

GROCERIES: _____ C-STORE: _____

DRINKING WATER: _____ NON-POTABLE WATER: _____

DUMP STATION: _____ DUMPSTER: _____

LAUNDRY: _____ SHOWERS: _____

FIREWOOD: _____ DOG PARK: _____

HIKING TRAILS: _____

ATTRACTIONS: _____

RANGER STATION: _____

OTHER: _____

_____

# IMAGES & JOURNAL NOTES

# CAMPSITE LOG

DATE(S): _____

CAMP: _____

LOCATION: _____

DIRECTIONS: _____

STATE: _____ ALTITUDE: _____ GPS: _____

ROAD CONDITIONS: _____

CELL SIGNAL: _____ WIFI: _____ WEBSITE: _____

WEATHER: _____ NOISE: _____ MAXIMUM STAY: _____

PROS: _____

CONS: _____

TIPS FOR NEXT STAY: _____

NOTES: _____
_____

☆ ☆ ☆ ☆ ☆

## ON-SITE CAMP AMENITIES:

- ☐ Picnic Tables
- ☐ Hiking Trails
- ☐ Boat Dock
- ☐ Pit Toilet
- ☐ Fire Pit
- ☐ Water
- ☐ Shade
- ☐ Views
- ☐ Nature Reserve
- ☐ Historic Sites
- ☐ Fishing
- ☐ OHV Trails
- ☐ Other _____

## NEARBY AMENITIES & NECESSITIES:

GAS: _____  PROPANE: _____

GROCERIES: _____  C-STORE: _____

DRINKING WATER: _____  NON-POTABLE WATER: _____

DUMP STATION: _____  DUMPSTER: _____

LAUNDRY: _____  SHOWERS: _____

FIREWOOD: _____  DOG PARK: _____

HIKING TRAILS: _____

ATTRACTIONS: _____

RANGER STATION: _____

OTHER: _____

# IMAGES & JOURNAL NOTES

# CAMPSITE LOG

DATE(S): _____

CAMP: _____

LOCATION: _____

DIRECTIONS: _____

STATE: _____ ALTITUDE: _____ GPS: _____

ROAD CONDITIONS: _____

CELL SIGNAL: _____ WIFI: _____ WEBSITE: _____

WEATHER: _____ NOISE: _____ MAXIMUM STAY: _____

PROS: _____

CONS: _____

TIPS FOR NEXT STAY: _____

NOTES: _____

_____

☆ ☆ ☆ ☆ ☆

## ON-SITE CAMP AMENITIES:

- ☐ Picnic Tables
- ☐ Hiking Trails
- ☐ Boat Dock
- ☐ Pit Toilet

- ☐ Fire Pit
- ☐ Water
- ☐ Shade
- ☐ Views

- ☐ Nature Reserve
- ☐ Historic Sites
- ☐ Fishing
- ☐ OHV Trails
- ☐ Other _____

## NEARBY AMENITIES & NECESSITIES:

GAS: _____ PROPANE: _____

GROCERIES: _____ C-STORE: _____

DRINKING WATER: _____ NON-POTABLE WATER: _____

DUMP STATION: _____ DUMPSTER: _____

LAUNDRY: _____ SHOWERS: _____

FIREWOOD: _____ DOG PARK: _____

HIKING TRAILS: _____

ATTRACTIONS: _____

RANGER STATION: _____

OTHER: _____

_____

# IMAGES & JOURNAL NOTES

# CAMPSITE LOG

DATE(S): _____

CAMP: _____

LOCATION: _____

DIRECTIONS: _____

STATE: _____ ALTITUDE: _____ GPS: _____

ROAD CONDITIONS: _____

CELL SIGNAL: _____ WIFI: _____ WEBSITE: _____

WEATHER: _____ NOISE: _____ MAXIMUM STAY: _____

PROS: _____

CONS: _____

TIPS FOR NEXT STAY: _____

NOTES: _____

☆ ☆ ☆ ☆ ☆

## ON-SITE CAMP AMENITIES:

☐ Nature Reserve

☐ Picnic Tables ☐ Fire Pit ☐ Historic Sites

☐ Hiking Trails ☐ Water ☐ Fishing

☐ Boat Dock ☐ Shade ☐ OHV Trails

☐ Pit Toilet ☐ Views ☐ Other _____

## NEARBY AMENITIES & NECESSITIES:

GAS: _____ PROPANE: _____

GROCERIES: _____ C-STORE: _____

DRINKING WATER: _____ NON-POTABLE WATER: _____

DUMP STATION: _____ DUMPSTER: _____

LAUNDRY: _____ SHOWERS: _____

FIREWOOD: _____ DOG PARK: _____

HIKING TRAILS: _____

ATTRACTIONS: _____

RANGER STATION: _____

OTHER: _____

# IMAGES & JOURNAL NOTES

# CAMPSITE LOG

DATE(S): _____

CAMP: _____

LOCATION: _____

DIRECTIONS: _____

STATE: _____ ALTITUDE: _____ GPS: _____

ROAD CONDITIONS: _____

CELL SIGNAL: _____ WIFI: _____ WEBSITE: _____

WEATHER: _____ NOISE: _____ MAXIMUM STAY: _____

PROS: _____

CONS: _____

TIPS FOR NEXT STAY: _____

NOTES: _____

_____

☆ ☆ ☆ ☆ ☆

## ON-SITE CAMP AMENITIES:

- ☐ Picnic Tables
- ☐ Hiking Trails
- ☐ Boat Dock
- ☐ Pit Toilet

- ☐ Fire Pit
- ☐ Water
- ☐ Shade
- ☐ Views

- ☐ Nature Reserve
- ☐ Historic Sites
- ☐ Fishing
- ☐ OHV Trails
- ☐ Other _____

## NEARBY AMENITIES & NECESSITIES:

GAS: _____ PROPANE: _____

GROCERIES: _____ C-STORE: _____

DRINKING WATER: _____ NON-POTABLE WATER: _____

DUMP STATION: _____ DUMPSTER: _____

LAUNDRY: _____ SHOWERS: _____

FIREWOOD: _____ DOG PARK: _____

HIKING TRAILS: _____

ATTRACTIONS: _____

RANGER STATION: _____

OTHER: _____

_____

# IMAGES & JOURNAL NOTES

# CAMPSITE LOG

DATE(S): _____

**CAMP:** _____

**LOCATION:** _____

**DIRECTIONS:** _____

**STATE:** _____ **ALTITUDE:** _____ **GPS:** _____

**ROAD CONDITIONS:** _____

**CELL SIGNAL:** _____ **WIFI:** _____ **WEBSITE:** _____

**WEATHER:** _____ **NOISE:** _____ **MAXIMUM STAY:** _____

**PROS:** _____

**CONS:** _____

**TIPS FOR NEXT STAY:** _____

**NOTES:** _____

☆ ☆ ☆ ☆ ☆

## ON-SITE CAMP AMENITIES:

- ☐ Picnic Tables
- ☐ Hiking Trails
- ☐ Boat Dock
- ☐ Pit Toilet

- ☐ Fire Pit
- ☐ Water
- ☐ Shade
- ☐ Views

- ☐ Nature Reserve
- ☐ Historic Sites
- ☐ Fishing
- ☐ OHV Trails
- ☐ Other _____

## NEARBY AMENITIES & NECESSITIES:

**GAS:** _____ **PROPANE:** _____

**GROCERIES:** _____ **C-STORE:** _____

**DRINKING WATER:** _____ **NON-POTABLE WATER:** _____

**DUMP STATION:** _____ **DUMPSTER:** _____

**LAUNDRY:** _____ **SHOWERS:** _____

**FIREWOOD:** _____ **DOG PARK:** _____

**HIKING TRAILS:** _____

**ATTRACTIONS:** _____

**RANGER STATION:** _____

**OTHER:** _____

# IMAGES & JOURNAL NOTES

# CAMPSITE LOG

DATE(S): _____

CAMP: _____

LOCATION: _____

DIRECTIONS: _____

STATE: _____ ALTITUDE: _____ GPS: _____

ROAD CONDITIONS: _____

CELL SIGNAL: _____ WIFI: _____ WEBSITE: _____

WEATHER: _____ NOISE: _____ MAXIMUM STAY: _____

PROS: _____

CONS: _____

TIPS FOR NEXT STAY: _____

NOTES: _____

☆ ☆ ☆ ☆ ☆

## ON-SITE CAMP AMENITIES:

- ☐ Picnic Tables
- ☐ Hiking Trails
- ☐ Boat Dock
- ☐ Pit Toilet
- ☐ Fire Pit
- ☐ Water
- ☐ Shade
- ☐ Views
- ☐ Nature Reserve
- ☐ Historic Sites
- ☐ Fishing
- ☐ OHV Trails
- ☐ Other _____

## NEARBY AMENITIES & NECESSITIES:

GAS: _____ PROPANE: _____

GROCERIES: _____ C-STORE: _____

DRINKING WATER: _____ NON-POTABLE WATER: _____

DUMP STATION: _____ DUMPSTER: _____

LAUNDRY: _____ SHOWERS: _____

FIREWOOD: _____ DOG PARK: _____

HIKING TRAILS: _____

ATTRACTIONS: _____

RANGER STATION: _____

OTHER: _____

# IMAGES & JOURNAL NOTES

# CAMPSITE LOG

DATE(S): _____

**CAMP:** _____

**LOCATION:** _____

**DIRECTIONS:** _____

**STATE:** _____ **ALTITUDE:** _____ **GPS:** _____

**ROAD CONDITIONS:** _____

**CELL SIGNAL:** _____ **WIFI:** _____ **WEBSITE:** _____

**WEATHER:** _____ **NOISE:** _____ **MAXIMUM STAY:** _____

**PROS:** _____

**CONS:** _____

**TIPS FOR NEXT STAY:** _____

**NOTES:** _____

☆ ☆ ☆ ☆ ☆

## ON-SITE CAMP AMENITIES:

☐ Picnic Tables        ☐ Fire Pit        ☐ Nature Reserve

☐ Hiking Trails        ☐ Water           ☐ Historic Sites

☐ Boat Dock            ☐ Shade           ☐ Fishing

☐ Pit Toilet           ☐ Views           ☐ OHV Trails

                                         ☐ Other _____

## NEARBY AMENITIES & NECESSITIES:

**GAS:** _____        **PROPANE:** _____

**GROCERIES:** _____  **C-STORE:** _____

**DRINKING WATER:** _____ **NON-POTABLE WATER:** _____

**DUMP STATION:** _____ **DUMPSTER:** _____

**LAUNDRY:** _____ **SHOWERS:** _____

**FIREWOOD:** _____ **DOG PARK:** _____

**HIKING TRAILS:** _____

**ATTRACTIONS:** _____

**RANGER STATION:** _____

**OTHER:** _____

# IMAGES & JOURNAL NOTES

# CAMPSITE LOG

DATE(S): _____

CAMP: _____

LOCATION: _____

DIRECTIONS: _____

STATE: _____ ALTITUDE: _____ GPS: _____

ROAD CONDITIONS: _____

CELL SIGNAL: _____ WIFI: _____ WEBSITE: _____

WEATHER: _____ NOISE: _____ MAXIMUM STAY: _____

PROS: _____

CONS: _____

TIPS FOR NEXT STAY: _____

NOTES: _____

_____

☆ ☆ ☆ ☆ ☆

## ON-SITE CAMP AMENITIES:

- ☐ Picnic Tables
- ☐ Hiking Trails
- ☐ Boat Dock
- ☐ Pit Toilet
- ☐ Fire Pit
- ☐ Water
- ☐ Shade
- ☐ Views
- ☐ Nature Reserve
- ☐ Historic Sites
- ☐ Fishing
- ☐ OHV Trails
- ☐ Other _____

## NEARBY AMENITIES & NECESSITIES:

GAS: _____ PROPANE: _____

GROCERIES: _____ C-STORE: _____

DRINKING WATER: _____ NON-POTABLE WATER: _____

DUMP STATION: _____ DUMPSTER: _____

LAUNDRY: _____ SHOWERS: _____

FIREWOOD: _____ DOG PARK: _____

HIKING TRAILS: _____

ATTRACTIONS: _____

RANGER STATION: _____

OTHER: _____

_____

# IMAGES & JOURNAL NOTES

# CAMPSITE LOG

DATE(S): _____

**CAMP:** _____

**LOCATION:** _____

**DIRECTIONS:** _____

**STATE:** _____ **ALTITUDE:** _____ **GPS:** _____

**ROAD CONDITIONS:** _____

**CELL SIGNAL:** _____ **WIFI:** _____ **WEBSITE:** _____

**WEATHER:** _____ **NOISE:** _____ **MAXIMUM STAY:** _____

**PROS:** _____

**CONS:** _____

**TIPS FOR NEXT STAY:** _____

**NOTES:** _____

☆ ☆ ☆ ☆ ☆

## ON-SITE CAMP AMENITIES:

- ☐ Picnic Tables
- ☐ Hiking Trails
- ☐ Boat Dock
- ☐ Pit Toilet
- ☐ Fire Pit
- ☐ Water
- ☐ Shade
- ☐ Views
- ☐ Nature Reserve
- ☐ Historic Sites
- ☐ Fishing
- ☐ OHV Trails
- ☐ Other _____

## NEARBY AMENITIES & NECESSITIES:

**GAS:** _____   **PROPANE:** _____

**GROCERIES:** _____   **C-STORE:** _____

**DRINKING WATER:** _____   **NON-POTABLE WATER:** _____

**DUMP STATION:** _____   **DUMPSTER:** _____

**LAUNDRY:** _____   **SHOWERS:** _____

**FIREWOOD:** _____   **DOG PARK:** _____

**HIKING TRAILS:** _____

**ATTRACTIONS:** _____

**RANGER STATION:** _____

**OTHER:** _____

# IMAGES & JOURNAL NOTES

# CAMPSITE LOG

DATE(S): _____

**CAMP:** _____

**LOCATION:** _____

**DIRECTIONS:** _____

**STATE:** _____ **ALTITUDE:** _____ **GPS:** _____

**ROAD CONDITIONS:** _____

**CELL SIGNAL:** _____ **WIFI:** _____ **WEBSITE:** _____

**WEATHER:** _____ **NOISE:** _____ **MAXIMUM STAY:** _____

**PROS:** _____

**CONS:** _____

**TIPS FOR NEXT STAY:** _____

**NOTES:** _____

☆ ☆ ☆ ☆ ☆

## ON-SITE CAMP AMENITIES:

- ☐ Picnic Tables
- ☐ Hiking Trails
- ☐ Boat Dock
- ☐ Pit Toilet
- ☐ Fire Pit
- ☐ Water
- ☐ Shade
- ☐ Views
- ☐ Nature Reserve
- ☐ Historic Sites
- ☐ Fishing
- ☐ OHV Trails
- ☐ Other _____

## NEARBY AMENITIES & NECESSITIES:

**GAS:** _____ **PROPANE:** _____

**GROCERIES:** _____ **C-STORE:** _____

**DRINKING WATER:** _____ **NON-POTABLE WATER:** _____

**DUMP STATION:** _____ **DUMPSTER:** _____

**LAUNDRY:** _____ **SHOWERS:** _____

**FIREWOOD:** _____ **DOG PARK:** _____

**HIKING TRAILS:** _____

**ATTRACTIONS:** _____

**RANGER STATION:** _____

**OTHER:** _____

# IMAGES & JOURNAL NOTES

# CAMPSITE LOG

DATE(S): _____

CAMP: _____

LOCATION: _____

DIRECTIONS: _____

STATE: _____ ALTITUDE: _____ GPS: _____

ROAD CONDITIONS: _____

CELL SIGNAL: _____ WIFI: _____ WEBSITE: _____

WEATHER: _____ NOISE: _____ MAXIMUM STAY: _____

PROS: _____

CONS: _____

TIPS FOR NEXT STAY: _____

NOTES: _____

☆ ☆ ☆ ☆ ☆

## ON-SITE CAMP AMENITIES:

- ☐ Picnic Tables
- ☐ Hiking Trails
- ☐ Boat Dock
- ☐ Pit Toilet
- ☐ Fire Pit
- ☐ Water
- ☐ Shade
- ☐ Views
- ☐ Nature Reserve
- ☐ Historic Sites
- ☐ Fishing
- ☐ OHV Trails
- ☐ Other _____

## NEARBY AMENITIES & NECESSITIES:

GAS: _____ PROPANE: _____

GROCERIES: _____ C-STORE: _____

DRINKING WATER: _____ NON-POTABLE WATER: _____

DUMP STATION: _____ DUMPSTER: _____

LAUNDRY: _____ SHOWERS: _____

FIREWOOD: _____ DOG PARK: _____

HIKING TRAILS: _____

ATTRACTIONS: _____

RANGER STATION: _____

OTHER: _____

# IMAGES & JOURNAL NOTES

# CAMPSITE LOG

DATE(S): _____

**CAMP:** _____

**LOCATION:** _____

**DIRECTIONS:** _____

**STATE:** _____ **ALTITUDE:** _____ **GPS:** _____

**ROAD CONDITIONS:** _____

**CELL SIGNAL:** _____ **WIFI:** _____ **WEBSITE:** _____

**WEATHER:** _____ **NOISE:** _____ **MAXIMUM STAY:** _____

**PROS:** _____

**CONS:** _____

**TIPS FOR NEXT STAY:** _____

**NOTES:** _____

☆ ☆ ☆ ☆ ☆

## ON-SITE CAMP AMENITIES:

- ☐ Picnic Tables
- ☐ Hiking Trails
- ☐ Boat Dock
- ☐ Pit Toilet

- ☐ Fire Pit
- ☐ Water
- ☐ Shade
- ☐ Views

- ☐ Nature Reserve
- ☐ Historic Sites
- ☐ Fishing
- ☐ OHV Trails
- ☐ Other _____

## NEARBY AMENITIES & NECESSITIES:

**GAS:** _____ **PROPANE:** _____

**GROCERIES:** _____ **C-STORE:** _____

**DRINKING WATER:** _____ **NON-POTABLE WATER:** _____

**DUMP STATION:** _____ **DUMPSTER:** _____

**LAUNDRY:** _____ **SHOWERS:** _____

**FIREWOOD:** _____ **DOG PARK:** _____

**HIKING TRAILS:** _____

**ATTRACTIONS:** _____

**RANGER STATION:** _____

**OTHER:** _____

# IMAGES & JOURNAL NOTES

# CAMPSITE LOG

DATE(S): _____

**CAMP:** _____

**LOCATION:** _____

**DIRECTIONS:** _____

**STATE:** _____ **ALTITUDE:** _____ **GPS:** _____

**ROAD CONDITIONS:** _____

**CELL SIGNAL:** _____ **WIFI:** _____ **WEBSITE:** _____

**WEATHER:** _____ **NOISE:** _____ **MAXIMUM STAY:** _____

**PROS:** _____

**CONS:** _____

**TIPS FOR NEXT STAY:** _____

**NOTES:** _____

☆ ☆ ☆ ☆ ☆

## ON-SITE CAMP AMENITIES:

- ☐ Picnic Tables
- ☐ Hiking Trails
- ☐ Boat Dock
- ☐ Pit Toilet
- ☐ Fire Pit
- ☐ Water
- ☐ Shade
- ☐ Views
- ☐ Nature Reserve
- ☐ Historic Sites
- ☐ Fishing
- ☐ OHV Trails
- ☐ Other _____

## NEARBY AMENITIES & NECESSITIES:

**GAS:** _____  **PROPANE:** _____

**GROCERIES:** _____  **C-STORE:** _____

**DRINKING WATER:** _____  **NON-POTABLE WATER:** _____

**DUMP STATION:** _____  **DUMPSTER:** _____

**LAUNDRY:** _____  **SHOWERS:** _____

**FIREWOOD:** _____  **DOG PARK:** _____

**HIKING TRAILS:** _____

**ATTRACTIONS:** _____

**RANGER STATION:** _____

**OTHER:** _____

# IMAGES & JOURNAL NOTES

# CAMPSITE LOG

DATE(S): _____

**CAMP:** _____

**LOCATION:** _____

**DIRECTIONS:** _____

**STATE:** _____ **ALTITUDE:** _____ **GPS:** _____

**ROAD CONDITIONS:** _____

**CELL SIGNAL:** _____ **WIFI:** _____ **WEBSITE:** _____

**WEATHER:** _____ **NOISE:** _____ **MAXIMUM STAY:** _____

**PROS:** _____

**CONS:** _____

**TIPS FOR NEXT STAY:** _____

**NOTES:** _____

☆ ☆ ☆ ☆ ☆

## ON-SITE CAMP AMENITIES:

- ☐ Picnic Tables
- ☐ Hiking Trails
- ☐ Boat Dock
- ☐ Pit Toilet
- ☐ Fire Pit
- ☐ Water
- ☐ Shade
- ☐ Views
- ☐ Nature Reserve
- ☐ Historic Sites
- ☐ Fishing
- ☐ OHV Trails
- ☐ Other _____

## NEARBY AMENITIES & NECESSITIES:

**GAS:** _____ **PROPANE:** _____

**GROCERIES:** _____ **C-STORE:** _____

**DRINKING WATER:** _____ **NON-POTABLE WATER:** _____

**DUMP STATION:** _____ **DUMPSTER:** _____

**LAUNDRY:** _____ **SHOWERS:** _____

**FIREWOOD:** _____ **DOG PARK:** _____

**HIKING TRAILS:** _____

**ATTRACTIONS:** _____

**RANGER STATION:** _____

**OTHER:** _____

# IMAGES & JOURNAL NOTES

# CAMPSITE LOG

DATE(S): _____

**CAMP:** _____

**LOCATION:** _____

**DIRECTIONS:** _____

**STATE:** _____ **ALTITUDE:** _____ **GPS:** _____

**ROAD CONDITIONS:** _____

**CELL SIGNAL:** _____ **WIFI:** _____ **WEBSITE:** _____

**WEATHER:** _____ **NOISE:** _____ **MAXIMUM STAY:** _____

**PROS:** _____

**CONS:** _____

**TIPS FOR NEXT STAY:** _____

**NOTES:** _____

☆ ☆ ☆ ☆ ☆

## ON-SITE CAMP AMENITIES:

- ☐ Picnic Tables
- ☐ Hiking Trails
- ☐ Boat Dock
- ☐ Pit Toilet
- ☐ Fire Pit
- ☐ Water
- ☐ Shade
- ☐ Views
- ☐ Nature Reserve
- ☐ Historic Sites
- ☐ Fishing
- ☐ OHV Trails
- ☐ Other _____

## NEARBY AMENITIES & NECESSITIES:

**GAS:** _____ **PROPANE:** _____

**GROCERIES:** _____ **C-STORE:** _____

**DRINKING WATER:** _____ **NON-POTABLE WATER:** _____

**DUMP STATION:** _____ **DUMPSTER:** _____

**LAUNDRY:** _____ **SHOWERS:** _____

**FIREWOOD:** _____ **DOG PARK:** _____

**HIKING TRAILS:** _____

**ATTRACTIONS:** _____

**RANGER STATION:** _____

**OTHER:** _____

# IMAGES & JOURNAL NOTES

# CAMPSITE LOG

DATE(S): _____

**CAMP:** _____

**LOCATION:** _____

**DIRECTIONS:** _____

**STATE:** _____ **ALTITUDE:** _____ **GPS:** _____

**ROAD CONDITIONS:** _____

**CELL SIGNAL:** _____ **WIFI:** _____ **WEBSITE:** _____

**WEATHER:** _____ **NOISE:** _____ **MAXIMUM STAY:** _____

**PROS:** _____

**CONS:** _____

**TIPS FOR NEXT STAY:** _____

**NOTES:** _____

☆ ☆ ☆ ☆ ☆

## ON-SITE CAMP AMENITIES:

- ☐ Picnic Tables
- ☐ Hiking Trails
- ☐ Boat Dock
- ☐ Pit Toilet

- ☐ Fire Pit
- ☐ Water
- ☐ Shade
- ☐ Views

- ☐ Nature Reserve
- ☐ Historic Sites
- ☐ Fishing
- ☐ OHV Trails
- ☐ Other _____

## NEARBY AMENITIES & NECESSITIES:

**GAS:** _____ **PROPANE:** _____

**GROCERIES:** _____ **C-STORE:** _____

**DRINKING WATER:** _____ **NON-POTABLE WATER:** _____

**DUMP STATION:** _____ **DUMPSTER:** _____

**LAUNDRY:** _____ **SHOWERS:** _____

**FIREWOOD:** _____ **DOG PARK:** _____

**HIKING TRAILS:** _____

**ATTRACTIONS:** _____

**RANGER STATION:** _____

**OTHER:** _____

# IMAGES & JOURNAL NOTES

# CAMPSITE LOG

DATE(S): _____

CAMP: _____

LOCATION: _____

DIRECTIONS: _____

STATE: _____ ALTITUDE: _____ GPS: _____

ROAD CONDITIONS: _____

CELL SIGNAL: _____ WIFI: _____ WEBSITE: _____

WEATHER: _____ NOISE: _____ MAXIMUM STAY: _____

PROS: _____

CONS: _____

TIPS FOR NEXT STAY: _____

NOTES: _____

☆ ☆ ☆ ☆ ☆

## ON-SITE CAMP AMENITIES:

☐ Picnic Tables ☐ Fire Pit ☐ Nature Reserve
☐ Hiking Trails ☐ Water ☐ Historic Sites
☐ Boat Dock ☐ Shade ☐ Fishing
☐ Pit Toilet ☐ Views ☐ OHV Trails
☐ Other _____

## NEARBY AMENITIES & NECESSITIES:

GAS: _____ PROPANE: _____

GROCERIES: _____ C-STORE: _____

DRINKING WATER: _____ NON-POTABLE WATER: _____

DUMP STATION: _____ DUMPSTER: _____

LAUNDRY: _____ SHOWERS: _____

FIREWOOD: _____ DOG PARK: _____

HIKING TRAILS: _____

ATTRACTIONS: _____

RANGER STATION: _____

OTHER: _____

# IMAGES & JOURNAL NOTES

# CAMPSITE LOG

DATE(S): _____

**CAMP:** _____

**LOCATION:** _____

DIRECTIONS: _____

STATE: _____ ALTITUDE: _____ GPS: _____

ROAD CONDITIONS: _____

CELL SIGNAL: _____ WIFI: _____ WEBSITE: _____

WEATHER: _____ NOISE: _____ MAXIMUM STAY: _____

PROS: _____

CONS: _____

TIPS FOR NEXT STAY: _____

NOTES: _____

☆ ☆ ☆ ☆ ☆

## ON-SITE CAMP AMENITIES:

- ☐ Picnic Tables
- ☐ Hiking Trails
- ☐ Boat Dock
- ☐ Pit Toilet
- ☐ Fire Pit
- ☐ Water
- ☐ Shade
- ☐ Views
- ☐ Nature Reserve
- ☐ Historic Sites
- ☐ Fishing
- ☐ OHV Trails
- ☐ Other _____

## NEARBY AMENITIES & NECESSITIES:

GAS: _____ PROPANE: _____

GROCERIES: _____ C-STORE: _____

DRINKING WATER: _____ NON-POTABLE WATER: _____

DUMP STATION: _____ DUMPSTER: _____

LAUNDRY: _____ SHOWERS: _____

FIREWOOD: _____ DOG PARK: _____

HIKING TRAILS: _____

ATTRACTIONS: _____

RANGER STATION: _____

OTHER: _____

# IMAGES & JOURNAL NOTES

# CAMPSITE LOG

DATE(S): _____

CAMP: _____

LOCATION: _____

DIRECTIONS: _____

STATE: _____ ALTITUDE: _____ GPS: _____

ROAD CONDITIONS: _____

CELL SIGNAL: _____ WIFI: _____ WEBSITE: _____

WEATHER: _____ NOISE: _____ MAXIMUM STAY: _____

PROS: _____

CONS: _____

TIPS FOR NEXT STAY: _____

NOTES: _____

☆ ☆ ☆ ☆ ☆

## ON-SITE CAMP AMENITIES:

- ☐ Picnic Tables
- ☐ Hiking Trails
- ☐ Boat Dock
- ☐ Pit Toilet
- ☐ Fire Pit
- ☐ Water
- ☐ Shade
- ☐ Views
- ☐ Nature Reserve
- ☐ Historic Sites
- ☐ Fishing
- ☐ OHV Trails
- ☐ Other _____

## NEARBY AMENITIES & NECESSITIES:

GAS: _____ PROPANE: _____

GROCERIES: _____ C-STORE: _____

DRINKING WATER: _____ NON-POTABLE WATER: _____

DUMP STATION: _____ DUMPSTER: _____

LAUNDRY: _____ SHOWERS: _____

FIREWOOD: _____ DOG PARK: _____

HIKING TRAILS: _____

ATTRACTIONS: _____

RANGER STATION: _____

OTHER: _____

# IMAGES & JOURNAL NOTES

# CAMPSITE LOG

DATE(S): _____

CAMP: _____

LOCATION: _____

DIRECTIONS: _____

STATE: _____ ALTITUDE: _____ GPS: _____

ROAD CONDITIONS: _____

CELL SIGNAL: _____ WIFI: _____ WEBSITE: _____

WEATHER: _____ NOISE: _____ MAXIMUM STAY: _____

PROS: _____

CONS: _____

TIPS FOR NEXT STAY: _____

NOTES: _____

☆ ☆ ☆ ☆ ☆

## ON-SITE CAMP AMENITIES:

- ☐ Picnic Tables
- ☐ Hiking Trails
- ☐ Boat Dock
- ☐ Pit Toilet
- ☐ Fire Pit
- ☐ Water
- ☐ Shade
- ☐ Views
- ☐ Nature Reserve
- ☐ Historic Sites
- ☐ Fishing
- ☐ OHV Trails
- ☐ Other _____

## NEARBY AMENITIES & NECESSITIES:

GAS: _____ PROPANE: _____

GROCERIES: _____ C-STORE: _____

DRINKING WATER: _____ NON-POTABLE WATER: _____

DUMP STATION: _____ DUMPSTER: _____

LAUNDRY: _____ SHOWERS: _____

FIREWOOD: _____ DOG PARK: _____

HIKING TRAILS: _____

ATTRACTIONS: _____

RANGER STATION: _____

OTHER: _____

# IMAGES & JOURNAL NOTES

_____
_____
_____
_____
_____
_____
_____
_____
_____
_____
_____
_____
_____
_____
_____

# CAMPSITE LOG

DATE(S): _____

**CAMP:** _____

**LOCATION:** _____

**DIRECTIONS:** _____

**STATE:** _____ **ALTITUDE:** _____ **GPS:** _____

**ROAD CONDITIONS:** _____

**CELL SIGNAL:** _____ **WIFI:** _____ **WEBSITE:** _____

**WEATHER:** _____ **NOISE:** _____ **MAXIMUM STAY:** _____

**PROS:** _____

**CONS:** _____

**TIPS FOR NEXT STAY:** _____

**NOTES:** _____

☆ ☆ ☆ ☆ ☆

## ON-SITE CAMP AMENITIES:

- ☐ Picnic Tables
- ☐ Hiking Trails
- ☐ Boat Dock
- ☐ Pit Toilet
- ☐ Fire Pit
- ☐ Water
- ☐ Shade
- ☐ Views
- ☐ Nature Reserve
- ☐ Historic Sites
- ☐ Fishing
- ☐ OHV Trails
- ☐ Other _____

## NEARBY AMENITIES & NECESSITIES:

**GAS:** _____ **PROPANE:** _____

**GROCERIES:** _____ **C-STORE:** _____

**DRINKING WATER:** _____ **NON-POTABLE WATER:** _____

**DUMP STATION:** _____ **DUMPSTER:** _____

**LAUNDRY:** _____ **SHOWERS:** _____

**FIREWOOD:** _____ **DOG PARK:** _____

**HIKING TRAILS:** _____

**ATTRACTIONS:** _____

**RANGER STATION:** _____

**OTHER:** _____

# IMAGES & JOURNAL NOTES

# CAMPSITE LOG

DATE(S): _____

**CAMP:** _____

**LOCATION:** _____

**DIRECTIONS:** _____

**STATE:** _____ **ALTITUDE:** _____ **GPS:** _____

**ROAD CONDITIONS:** _____

**CELL SIGNAL:** _____ **WIFI:** _____ **WEBSITE:** _____

**WEATHER:** _____ **NOISE:** _____ **MAXIMUM STAY:** _____

**PROS:** _____

**CONS:** _____

**TIPS FOR NEXT STAY:** _____

**NOTES:** _____

☆ ☆ ☆ ☆ ☆

## ON-SITE CAMP AMENITIES:

☐ Picnic Tables        ☐ Fire Pit          ☐ Nature Reserve
☐ Hiking Trails        ☐ Water             ☐ Historic Sites
☐ Boat Dock            ☐ Shade             ☐ Fishing
☐ Pit Toilet           ☐ Views             ☐ OHV Trails
                                           ☐ Other _____

## NEARBY AMENITIES & NECESSITIES:

**GAS:** _____ **PROPANE:** _____

**GROCERIES:** _____ **C-STORE:** _____

**DRINKING WATER:** _____ **NON-POTABLE WATER:** _____

**DUMP STATION:** _____ **DUMPSTER:** _____

**LAUNDRY:** _____ **SHOWERS:** _____

**FIREWOOD:** _____ **DOG PARK:** _____

**HIKING TRAILS:** _____

**ATTRACTIONS:** _____

**RANGER STATION:** _____

**OTHER:** _____

# IMAGES & JOURNAL NOTES

# CAMPSITE LOG

DATE(S): _____

**CAMP:** _____

**LOCATION:** _____

DIRECTIONS: _____

STATE: _____ ALTITUDE: _____ GPS: _____

ROAD CONDITIONS: _____

CELL SIGNAL: _____ WIFI: _____ WEBSITE: _____

WEATHER: _____ NOISE: _____ MAXIMUM STAY: _____

PROS: _____

CONS: _____

TIPS FOR NEXT STAY: _____

NOTES: _____

☆ ☆ ☆ ☆ ☆

## ON-SITE CAMP AMENITIES:

☐ Nature Reserve

☐ Picnic Tables    ☐ Fire Pit    ☐ Historic Sites

☐ Hiking Trails    ☐ Water    ☐ Fishing

☐ Boat Dock    ☐ Shade    ☐ OHV Trails

☐ Pit Toilet    ☐ Views    ☐ Other _____

## NEARBY AMENITIES & NECESSITIES:

GAS: _____ PROPANE: _____

GROCERIES: _____ C-STORE: _____

DRINKING WATER: _____ NON-POTABLE WATER: _____

DUMP STATION: _____ DUMPSTER: _____

LAUNDRY: _____ SHOWERS: _____

FIREWOOD: _____ DOG PARK: _____

HIKING TRAILS: _____

ATTRACTIONS: _____

RANGER STATION: _____

OTHER: _____

# IMAGES & JOURNAL NOTES

# CAMPSITE LOG

DATE(S): _____

CAMP: _____

LOCATION: _____

DIRECTIONS: _____

STATE: _____ ALTITUDE: _____ GPS: _____

ROAD CONDITIONS: _____

CELL SIGNAL: _____ WIFI: _____ WEBSITE: _____

WEATHER: _____ NOISE: _____ MAXIMUM STAY: _____

PROS: _____

CONS: _____

TIPS FOR NEXT STAY: _____

NOTES: _____

☆ ☆ ☆ ☆ ☆

## ON-SITE CAMP AMENITIES:

- ☐ Picnic Tables
- ☐ Hiking Trails
- ☐ Boat Dock
- ☐ Pit Toilet

- ☐ Fire Pit
- ☐ Water
- ☐ Shade
- ☐ Views

- ☐ Nature Reserve
- ☐ Historic Sites
- ☐ Fishing
- ☐ OHV Trails
- ☐ Other _____

## NEARBY AMENITIES & NECESSITIES:

GAS: _____ PROPANE: _____

GROCERIES: _____ C-STORE: _____

DRINKING WATER: _____ NON-POTABLE WATER: _____

DUMP STATION: _____ DUMPSTER: _____

LAUNDRY: _____ SHOWERS: _____

FIREWOOD: _____ DOG PARK: _____

HIKING TRAILS: _____

ATTRACTIONS: _____

RANGER STATION: _____

OTHER: _____

# IMAGES & JOURNAL NOTES

# CAMPSITE LOG

DATE(S): _____

**CAMP:** _____

**LOCATION:** _____

**DIRECTIONS:** _____

**STATE:** _____ **ALTITUDE:** _____ **GPS:** _____

**ROAD CONDITIONS:** _____

**CELL SIGNAL:** _____ **WIFI:** _____ **WEBSITE:** _____

**WEATHER:** _____ **NOISE:** _____ **MAXIMUM STAY:** _____

**PROS:** _____

**CONS:** _____

**TIPS FOR NEXT STAY:** _____

**NOTES:** _____

☆ ☆ ☆ ☆ ☆

## ON-SITE CAMP AMENITIES:

☐ Nature Reserve

☐ Picnic Tables      ☐ Fire Pit       ☐ Historic Sites

☐ Hiking Trails      ☐ Water          ☐ Fishing

☐ Boat Dock          ☐ Shade          ☐ OHV Trails

☐ Pit Toilet         ☐ Views          ☐ Other _____

## NEARBY AMENITIES & NECESSITIES:

**GAS:** _____      **PROPANE:** _____

**GROCERIES:** _____      **C-STORE:** _____

**DRINKING WATER:** _____      **NON-POTABLE WATER:** _____

**DUMP STATION:** _____      **DUMPSTER:** _____

**LAUNDRY:** _____      **SHOWERS:** _____

**FIREWOOD:** _____      **DOG PARK:** _____

**HIKING TRAILS:** _____

**ATTRACTIONS:** _____

**RANGER STATION:** _____

**OTHER:** _____

# IMAGES & JOURNAL NOTES

# CAMPSITE LOG

DATE(S): _____

**CAMP:** _____

**LOCATION:** _____

**DIRECTIONS:** _____

**STATE:** _____ **ALTITUDE:** _____ **GPS:** _____

**ROAD CONDITIONS:** _____

**CELL SIGNAL:** _____ **WIFI:** _____ **WEBSITE:** _____

**WEATHER:** _____ **NOISE:** _____ **MAXIMUM STAY:** _____

**PROS:** _____

**CONS:** _____

**TIPS FOR NEXT STAY:** _____

**NOTES:** _____

☆ ☆ ☆ ☆ ☆

## ON-SITE CAMP AMENITIES:

- ☐ Picnic Tables
- ☐ Hiking Trails
- ☐ Boat Dock
- ☐ Pit Toilet
- ☐ Fire Pit
- ☐ Water
- ☐ Shade
- ☐ Views
- ☐ Nature Reserve
- ☐ Historic Sites
- ☐ Fishing
- ☐ OHV Trails
- ☐ Other _____

## NEARBY AMENITIES & NECESSITIES:

**GAS:** _____ **PROPANE:** _____

**GROCERIES:** _____ **C-STORE:** _____

**DRINKING WATER:** _____ **NON-POTABLE WATER:** _____

**DUMP STATION:** _____ **DUMPSTER:** _____

**LAUNDRY:** _____ **SHOWERS:** _____

**FIREWOOD:** _____ **DOG PARK:** _____

**HIKING TRAILS:** _____

**ATTRACTIONS:** _____

**RANGER STATION:** _____

**OTHER:** _____

# IMAGES & JOURNAL NOTES

# CAMPSITE LOG

DATE(S): _____

**CAMP:** _____

**LOCATION:** _____

**DIRECTIONS:** _____

**STATE:** _____ **ALTITUDE:** _____ **GPS:** _____

**ROAD CONDITIONS:** _____

**CELL SIGNAL:** _____ **WIFI:** _____ **WEBSITE:** _____

**WEATHER:** _____ **NOISE:** _____ **MAXIMUM STAY:** _____

**PROS:** _____

**CONS:** _____

**TIPS FOR NEXT STAY:** _____

**NOTES:** _____

☆ ☆ ☆ ☆ ☆

## ON-SITE CAMP AMENITIES:

- ☐ Picnic Tables
- ☐ Hiking Trails
- ☐ Boat Dock
- ☐ Pit Toilet

- ☐ Fire Pit
- ☐ Water
- ☐ Shade
- ☐ Views

- ☐ Nature Reserve
- ☐ Historic Sites
- ☐ Fishing
- ☐ OHV Trails
- ☐ Other _____

## NEARBY AMENITIES & NECESSITIES:

**GAS:** _____

**PROPANE:** _____

**GROCERIES:** _____

**C-STORE:** _____

**DRINKING WATER:** _____

**NON-POTABLE WATER:** _____

**DUMP STATION:** _____

**DUMPSTER:** _____

**LAUNDRY:** _____

**SHOWERS:** _____

**FIREWOOD:** _____

**DOG PARK:** _____

**HIKING TRAILS:** _____

**ATTRACTIONS:** _____

**RANGER STATION:** _____

**OTHER:** _____

# IMAGES & JOURNAL NOTES

# CAMPSITE LOG

DATE(S): _____

**CAMP:** _____

**LOCATION:** _____

DIRECTIONS: _____

STATE: _____  ALTITUDE: _____  GPS: _____

ROAD CONDITIONS: _____

CELL SIGNAL: _____  WIFI: _____  WEBSITE: _____

WEATHER: _____  NOISE: _____  MAXIMUM STAY: _____

PROS: _____

CONS: _____

TIPS FOR NEXT STAY: _____

NOTES: _____

☆ ☆ ☆ ☆ ☆

## ON-SITE CAMP AMENITIES:

- ☐ Picnic Tables
- ☐ Hiking Trails
- ☐ Boat Dock
- ☐ Pit Toilet
- ☐ Fire Pit
- ☐ Water
- ☐ Shade
- ☐ Views
- ☐ Nature Reserve
- ☐ Historic Sites
- ☐ Fishing
- ☐ OHV Trails
- ☐ Other _____

## NEARBY AMENITIES & NECESSITIES:

GAS: _____  PROPANE: _____

GROCERIES: _____  C-STORE: _____

DRINKING WATER: _____  NON-POTABLE WATER: _____

DUMP STATION: _____  DUMPSTER: _____

LAUNDRY: _____  SHOWERS: _____

FIREWOOD: _____  DOG PARK: _____

HIKING TRAILS: _____

ATTRACTIONS: _____

RANGER STATION: _____

OTHER: _____

# IMAGES & JOURNAL NOTES

# CAMPSITE LOG

DATE(S): _____

**CAMP:** _____

**LOCATION:** _____

**DIRECTIONS:** _____

**STATE:** _____ **ALTITUDE:** _____ **GPS:** _____

**ROAD CONDITIONS:** _____

**CELL SIGNAL:** _____ **WIFI:** _____ **WEBSITE:** _____

**WEATHER:** _____ **NOISE:** _____ **MAXIMUM STAY:** _____

**PROS:** _____

**CONS:** _____

**TIPS FOR NEXT STAY:** _____

**NOTES:** _____

☆ ☆ ☆ ☆ ☆

## ON-SITE CAMP AMENITIES:

- ☐ Picnic Tables
- ☐ Hiking Trails
- ☐ Boat Dock
- ☐ Pit Toilet
- ☐ Fire Pit
- ☐ Water
- ☐ Shade
- ☐ Views
- ☐ Nature Reserve
- ☐ Historic Sites
- ☐ Fishing
- ☐ OHV Trails
- ☐ Other _____

## NEARBY AMENITIES & NECESSITIES:

**GAS:** _____ **PROPANE:** _____

**GROCERIES:** _____ **C-STORE:** _____

**DRINKING WATER:** _____ **NON-POTABLE WATER:** _____

**DUMP STATION:** _____ **DUMPSTER:** _____

**LAUNDRY:** _____ **SHOWERS:** _____

**FIREWOOD:** _____ **DOG PARK:** _____

**HIKING TRAILS:** _____

**ATTRACTIONS:** _____

**RANGER STATION:** _____

**OTHER:** _____

# IMAGES & JOURNAL NOTES

# CAMPSITE LOG

DATE(S): _____

**CAMP:** _____

**LOCATION:** _____

**DIRECTIONS:** _____

**STATE:** _____ **ALTITUDE:** _____ **GPS:** _____

**ROAD CONDITIONS:** _____

**CELL SIGNAL:** _____ **WIFI:** _____ **WEBSITE:** _____

**WEATHER:** _____ **NOISE:** _____ **MAXIMUM STAY:** _____

**PROS:** _____

**CONS:** _____

**TIPS FOR NEXT STAY:** _____

**NOTES:** _____

☆ ☆ ☆ ☆ ☆

## ON-SITE CAMP AMENITIES:

- ☐ Picnic Tables
- ☐ Hiking Trails
- ☐ Boat Dock
- ☐ Pit Toilet
- ☐ Fire Pit
- ☐ Water
- ☐ Shade
- ☐ Views
- ☐ Nature Reserve
- ☐ Historic Sites
- ☐ Fishing
- ☐ OHV Trails
- ☐ Other _____

## NEARBY AMENITIES & NECESSITIES:

**GAS:** _____  **PROPANE:** _____

**GROCERIES:** _____  **C-STORE:** _____

**DRINKING WATER:** _____  **NON-POTABLE WATER:** _____

**DUMP STATION:** _____  **DUMPSTER:** _____

**LAUNDRY:** _____  **SHOWERS:** _____

**FIREWOOD:** _____  **DOG PARK:** _____

**HIKING TRAILS:** _____

**ATTRACTIONS:** _____

**RANGER STATION:** _____

**OTHER:** _____

# IMAGES & JOURNAL NOTES

# CAMPSITE LOG

DATE(S): _____

**CAMP:** _____

**LOCATION:** _____

**DIRECTIONS:** _____

**STATE:** _____ **ALTITUDE:** _____ **GPS:** _____

**ROAD CONDITIONS:** _____

**CELL SIGNAL:** _____ **WIFI:** _____ **WEBSITE:** _____

**WEATHER:** _____ **NOISE:** _____ **MAXIMUM STAY:** _____

**PROS:** _____

**CONS:** _____

**TIPS FOR NEXT STAY:** _____

**NOTES:** _____

☆ ☆ ☆ ☆ ☆

## ON-SITE CAMP AMENITIES:

- ☐ Picnic Tables
- ☐ Hiking Trails
- ☐ Boat Dock
- ☐ Pit Toilet
- ☐ Fire Pit
- ☐ Water
- ☐ Shade
- ☐ Views
- ☐ Nature Reserve
- ☐ Historic Sites
- ☐ Fishing
- ☐ OHV Trails
- ☐ Other _____

## NEARBY AMENITIES & NECESSITIES:

**GAS:** _____ **PROPANE:** _____

**GROCERIES:** _____ **C-STORE:** _____

**DRINKING WATER:** _____ **NON-POTABLE WATER:** _____

**DUMP STATION:** _____ **DUMPSTER:** _____

**LAUNDRY:** _____ **SHOWERS:** _____

**FIREWOOD:** _____ **DOG PARK:** _____

**HIKING TRAILS:** _____

**ATTRACTIONS:** _____

**RANGER STATION:** _____

**OTHER:** _____

# IMAGES & JOURNAL NOTES

# CAMPSITE LOG

DATE(S): _____

**CAMP:** _____

**LOCATION:** _____

**DIRECTIONS:** _____

**STATE:** _____ **ALTITUDE:** _____ **GPS:** _____

**ROAD CONDITIONS:** _____

**CELL SIGNAL:** _____ **WIFI:** _____ **WEBSITE:** _____

**WEATHER:** _____ **NOISE:** _____ **MAXIMUM STAY:** _____

**PROS:** _____

**CONS:** _____

**TIPS FOR NEXT STAY:** _____

**NOTES:** _____

☆ ☆ ☆ ☆ ☆

## ON-SITE CAMP AMENITIES:

☐ Picnic Tables     ☐ Fire Pit     ☐ Nature Reserve

☐ Hiking Trails     ☐ Water     ☐ Historic Sites

☐ Boat Dock     ☐ Shade     ☐ Fishing

☐ Pit Toilet     ☐ Views     ☐ OHV Trails

    ☐ Other _____

## NEARBY AMENITIES & NECESSITIES:

**GAS:** _____     **PROPANE:** _____

**GROCERIES:** _____     **C-STORE:** _____

**DRINKING WATER:** _____     **NON-POTABLE WATER:** _____

**DUMP STATION:** _____     **DUMPSTER:** _____

**LAUNDRY:** _____     **SHOWERS:** _____

**FIREWOOD:** _____     **DOG PARK:** _____

**HIKING TRAILS:** _____

**ATTRACTIONS:** _____

**RANGER STATION:** _____

**OTHER:** _____

# IMAGES & JOURNAL NOTES

# CAMPSITE LOG

DATE(S): _____

**CAMP:** _____

**LOCATION:** _____

**DIRECTIONS:** _____

**STATE:** _____ **ALTITUDE:** _____ **GPS:** _____

**ROAD CONDITIONS:** _____

**CELL SIGNAL:** _____ **WIFI:** _____ **WEBSITE:** _____

**WEATHER:** _____ **NOISE:** _____ **MAXIMUM STAY:** _____

**PROS:** _____

**CONS:** _____

**TIPS FOR NEXT STAY:** _____

**NOTES:** _____

☆ ☆ ☆ ☆ ☆

## ON-SITE CAMP AMENITIES:

☐ Picnic Tables    ☐ Fire Pit    ☐ Nature Reserve

☐ Hiking Trails    ☐ Water    ☐ Historic Sites

☐ Boat Dock    ☐ Shade    ☐ Fishing

☐ Pit Toilet    ☐ Views    ☐ OHV Trails

☐ Other _____

## NEARBY AMENITIES & NECESSITIES:

**GAS:** _____ **PROPANE:** _____

**GROCERIES:** _____ **C-STORE:** _____

**DRINKING WATER:** _____ **NON-POTABLE WATER:** _____

**DUMP STATION:** _____ **DUMPSTER:** _____

**LAUNDRY:** _____ **SHOWERS:** _____

**FIREWOOD:** _____ **DOG PARK:** _____

**HIKING TRAILS:** _____

**ATTRACTIONS:** _____

**RANGER STATION:** _____

**OTHER:** _____

# IMAGES & JOURNAL NOTES

# CAMPSITE LOG

DATE(S): _____

**CAMP:** _____

**LOCATION:** _____

**DIRECTIONS:** _____

**STATE:** _____ **ALTITUDE:** _____ **GPS:** _____

**ROAD CONDITIONS:** _____

**CELL SIGNAL:** _____ **WIFI:** _____ **WEBSITE:** _____

**WEATHER:** _____ **NOISE:** _____ **MAXIMUM STAY:** _____

**PROS:** _____

**CONS:** _____

**TIPS FOR NEXT STAY:** _____

**NOTES:** _____

☆ ☆ ☆ ☆ ☆

## ON-SITE CAMP AMENITIES:

☐ Nature Reserve

☐ Picnic Tables   ☐ Fire Pit   ☐ Historic Sites

☐ Hiking Trails   ☐ Water   ☐ Fishing

☐ Boat Dock   ☐ Shade   ☐ OHV Trails

☐ Pit Toilet   ☐ Views   ☐ Other _____

## NEARBY AMENITIES & NECESSITIES:

**GAS:** _____   **PROPANE:** _____

**GROCERIES:** _____   **C-STORE:** _____

**DRINKING WATER:** _____   **NON-POTABLE WATER:** _____

**DUMP STATION:** _____   **DUMPSTER:** _____

**LAUNDRY:** _____   **SHOWERS:** _____

**FIREWOOD:** _____   **DOG PARK:** _____

**HIKING TRAILS:** _____

**ATTRACTIONS:** _____

**RANGER STATION:** _____

**OTHER:** _____

# IMAGES & JOURNAL NOTES

# CAMPSITE LOG

DATE(S): _____

**CAMP:** _____

**LOCATION:** _____

**DIRECTIONS:** _____

**STATE:** _____ **ALTITUDE:** _____ **GPS:** _____

**ROAD CONDITIONS:** _____

**CELL SIGNAL:** _____ **WIFI:** _____ **WEBSITE:** _____

**WEATHER:** _____ **NOISE:** _____ **MAXIMUM STAY:** _____

**PROS:** _____

**CONS:** _____

**TIPS FOR NEXT STAY:** _____

**NOTES:** _____

☆ ☆ ☆ ☆ ☆

## ON-SITE CAMP AMENITIES:

☐ Picnic Tables        ☐ Fire Pit        ☐ Nature Reserve
☐ Hiking Trails        ☐ Water           ☐ Historic Sites
☐ Boat Dock            ☐ Shade           ☐ Fishing
☐ Pit Toilet           ☐ Views           ☐ OHV Trails
                                          ☐ Other _____

## NEARBY AMENITIES & NECESSITIES:

**GAS:** _____ **PROPANE:** _____

**GROCERIES:** _____ **C-STORE:** _____

**DRINKING WATER:** _____ **NON-POTABLE WATER:** _____

**DUMP STATION:** _____ **DUMPSTER:** _____

**LAUNDRY:** _____ **SHOWERS:** _____

**FIREWOOD:** _____ **DOG PARK:** _____

**HIKING TRAILS:** _____

**ATTRACTIONS:** _____

**RANGER STATION:** _____

**OTHER:** _____

# IMAGES & JOURNAL NOTES

# CAMPSITE LOG

DATE(S): _____

**CAMP:** _____

**LOCATION:** _____

DIRECTIONS: _____

STATE: _____ ALTITUDE: _____ GPS: _____

ROAD CONDITIONS: _____

CELL SIGNAL: _____ WIFI: _____ WEBSITE: _____

WEATHER: _____ NOISE: _____ MAXIMUM STAY: _____

PROS: _____

CONS: _____

TIPS FOR NEXT STAY: _____

NOTES: _____

☆ ☆ ☆ ☆ ☆

## ON-SITE CAMP AMENITIES:

- ☐ Picnic Tables
- ☐ Hiking Trails
- ☐ Boat Dock
- ☐ Pit Toilet

- ☐ Fire Pit
- ☐ Water
- ☐ Shade
- ☐ Views

- ☐ Nature Reserve
- ☐ Historic Sites
- ☐ Fishing
- ☐ OHV Trails
- ☐ Other _____

## NEARBY AMENITIES & NECESSITIES:

GAS: _____ PROPANE: _____

GROCERIES: _____ C-STORE: _____

DRINKING WATER: _____ NON-POTABLE WATER: _____

DUMP STATION: _____ DUMPSTER: _____

LAUNDRY: _____ SHOWERS: _____

FIREWOOD: _____ DOG PARK: _____

HIKING TRAILS: _____

ATTRACTIONS: _____

RANGER STATION: _____

OTHER: _____

# IMAGES & JOURNAL NOTES

# CAMPSITE LOG

DATE(S): _____

**CAMP:** _____

**LOCATION:** _____

**DIRECTIONS:** _____

**STATE:** _____ **ALTITUDE:** _____ **GPS:** _____

**ROAD CONDITIONS:** _____

**CELL SIGNAL:** _____ **WIFI:** _____ **WEBSITE:** _____

**WEATHER:** _____ **NOISE:** _____ **MAXIMUM STAY:** _____

**PROS:** _____

**CONS:** _____

**TIPS FOR NEXT STAY:** _____

**NOTES:** _____

☆ ☆ ☆ ☆ ☆

## ON-SITE CAMP AMENITIES:

- ☐ Picnic Tables
- ☐ Hiking Trails
- ☐ Boat Dock
- ☐ Pit Toilet

- ☐ Fire Pit
- ☐ Water
- ☐ Shade
- ☐ Views

- ☐ Nature Reserve
- ☐ Historic Sites
- ☐ Fishing
- ☐ OHV Trails
- ☐ Other _____

## NEARBY AMENITIES & NECESSITIES:

**GAS:** _____ **PROPANE:** _____

**GROCERIES:** _____ **C-STORE:** _____

**DRINKING WATER:** _____ **NON-POTABLE WATER:** _____

**DUMP STATION:** _____ **DUMPSTER:** _____

**LAUNDRY:** _____ **SHOWERS:** _____

**FIREWOOD:** _____ **DOG PARK:** _____

**HIKING TRAILS:** _____

**ATTRACTIONS:** _____

**RANGER STATION:** _____

**OTHER:** _____

# IMAGES & JOURNAL NOTES

# CAMPSITE LOG

DATE(S): _____

**CAMP:** _____

**LOCATION:** _____

**DIRECTIONS:** _____

**STATE:** _____ **ALTITUDE:** _____ **GPS:** _____

**ROAD CONDITIONS:** _____

**CELL SIGNAL:** _____ **WIFI:** _____ **WEBSITE:** _____

**WEATHER:** _____ **NOISE:** _____ **MAXIMUM STAY:** _____

**PROS:** _____

**CONS:** _____

**TIPS FOR NEXT STAY:** _____

**NOTES:** _____

☆ ☆ ☆ ☆ ☆

## ON-SITE CAMP AMENITIES:
- ☐ Picnic Tables
- ☐ Hiking Trails
- ☐ Boat Dock
- ☐ Pit Toilet
- ☐ Fire Pit
- ☐ Water
- ☐ Shade
- ☐ Views
- ☐ Nature Reserve
- ☐ Historic Sites
- ☐ Fishing
- ☐ OHV Trails
- ☐ Other _____

## NEARBY AMENITIES & NECESSITIES:

**GAS:** _____ **PROPANE:** _____

**GROCERIES:** _____ **C-STORE:** _____

**DRINKING WATER:** _____ **NON-POTABLE WATER:** _____

**DUMP STATION:** _____ **DUMPSTER:** _____

**LAUNDRY:** _____ **SHOWERS:** _____

**FIREWOOD:** _____ **DOG PARK:** _____

**HIKING TRAILS:** _____

**ATTRACTIONS:** _____

**RANGER STATION:** _____

**OTHER:** _____

# IMAGES & JOURNAL NOTES

# CAMPSITE LOG

DATE(S): _____

CAMP: _____

LOCATION: _____

DIRECTIONS: _____

STATE: _____ ALTITUDE: _____ GPS: _____

ROAD CONDITIONS: _____

CELL SIGNAL: _____ WIFI: _____ WEBSITE: _____

WEATHER: _____ NOISE: _____ MAXIMUM STAY: _____

PROS: _____

CONS: _____

TIPS FOR NEXT STAY: _____

NOTES: _____

☆ ☆ ☆ ☆ ☆

## ON-SITE CAMP AMENITIES:

- ☐ Picnic Tables
- ☐ Hiking Trails
- ☐ Boat Dock
- ☐ Pit Toilet

- ☐ Fire Pit
- ☐ Water
- ☐ Shade
- ☐ Views

- ☐ Nature Reserve
- ☐ Historic Sites
- ☐ Fishing
- ☐ OHV Trails
- ☐ Other _____

## NEARBY AMENITIES & NECESSITIES:

GAS: _____ PROPANE: _____

GROCERIES: _____ C-STORE: _____

DRINKING WATER: _____ NON-POTABLE WATER: _____

DUMP STATION: _____ DUMPSTER: _____

LAUNDRY: _____ SHOWERS: _____

FIREWOOD: _____ DOG PARK: _____

HIKING TRAILS: _____

ATTRACTIONS: _____

RANGER STATION: _____

OTHER: _____

# IMAGES & JOURNAL NOTES

# CAMPSITE LOG

DATE(S): _____

**CAMP:** _____

**LOCATION:** _____

**DIRECTIONS:** _____

**STATE:** _____ **ALTITUDE:** _____ **GPS:** _____

**ROAD CONDITIONS:** _____

**CELL SIGNAL:** _____ **WIFI:** _____ **WEBSITE:** _____

**WEATHER:** _____ **NOISE:** _____ **MAXIMUM STAY:** _____

**PROS:** _____

**CONS:** _____

**TIPS FOR NEXT STAY:** _____

**NOTES:** _____

☆ ☆ ☆ ☆ ☆

## ON-SITE CAMP AMENITIES:

☐ Picnic Tables        ☐ Fire Pit        ☐ Nature Reserve
☐ Hiking Trails        ☐ Water           ☐ Historic Sites
☐ Boat Dock            ☐ Shade           ☐ Fishing
☐ Pit Toilet           ☐ Views           ☐ OHV Trails
                                          ☐ Other _____

## NEARBY AMENITIES & NECESSITIES:

**GAS:** _____ **PROPANE:** _____

**GROCERIES:** _____ **C-STORE:** _____

**DRINKING WATER:** _____ **NON-POTABLE WATER:** _____

**DUMP STATION:** _____ **DUMPSTER:** _____

**LAUNDRY:** _____ **SHOWERS:** _____

**FIREWOOD:** _____ **DOG PARK:** _____

**HIKING TRAILS:** _____

**ATTRACTIONS:** _____

**RANGER STATION:** _____

**OTHER:** _____

# IMAGES & JOURNAL NOTES

# CAMPSITE LOG

DATE(S): _____

**CAMP:** _____

**LOCATION:** _____

**DIRECTIONS:** _____

**STATE:** _____ **ALTITUDE:** _____ **GPS:** _____

**ROAD CONDITIONS:** _____

**CELL SIGNAL:** _____ **WIFI:** _____ **WEBSITE:** _____

**WEATHER:** _____ **NOISE:** _____ **MAXIMUM STAY:** _____

**PROS:** _____

**CONS:** _____

**TIPS FOR NEXT STAY:** _____

**NOTES:** _____

☆ ☆ ☆ ☆ ☆

## ON-SITE CAMP AMENITIES:

- ☐ Picnic Tables
- ☐ Hiking Trails
- ☐ Boat Dock
- ☐ Pit Toilet
- ☐ Fire Pit
- ☐ Water
- ☐ Shade
- ☐ Views
- ☐ Nature Reserve
- ☐ Historic Sites
- ☐ Fishing
- ☐ OHV Trails
- ☐ Other _____

## NEARBY AMENITIES & NECESSITIES:

**GAS:** _____ **PROPANE:** _____

**GROCERIES:** _____ **C-STORE:** _____

**DRINKING WATER:** _____ **NON-POTABLE WATER:** _____

**DUMP STATION:** _____ **DUMPSTER:** _____

**LAUNDRY:** _____ **SHOWERS:** _____

**FIREWOOD:** _____ **DOG PARK:** _____

**HIKING TRAILS:** _____

**ATTRACTIONS:** _____

**RANGER STATION:** _____

**OTHER:** _____

# IMAGES & JOURNAL NOTES

# CAMPSITE LOG

DATE(S): _____

**CAMP:** _____

**LOCATION:** _____

DIRECTIONS: _____

STATE: _____ ALTITUDE: _____ GPS: _____

ROAD CONDITIONS: _____

CELL SIGNAL: _____ WIFI: _____ WEBSITE: _____

WEATHER: _____ NOISE: _____ MAXIMUM STAY: _____

PROS: _____

CONS: _____

TIPS FOR NEXT STAY: _____

NOTES: _____

☆ ☆ ☆ ☆ ☆

## ON-SITE CAMP AMENITIES:

- ☐ Picnic Tables
- ☐ Hiking Trails
- ☐ Boat Dock
- ☐ Pit Toilet

- ☐ Fire Pit
- ☐ Water
- ☐ Shade
- ☐ Views

- ☐ Nature Reserve
- ☐ Historic Sites
- ☐ Fishing
- ☐ OHV Trails
- ☐ Other _____

## NEARBY AMENITIES & NECESSITIES:

GAS: _____ PROPANE: _____

GROCERIES: _____ C-STORE: _____

DRINKING WATER: _____ NON-POTABLE WATER: _____

DUMP STATION: _____ DUMPSTER: _____

LAUNDRY: _____ SHOWERS: _____

FIREWOOD: _____ DOG PARK: _____

HIKING TRAILS: _____

ATTRACTIONS: _____

RANGER STATION: _____

OTHER: _____

# IMAGES & JOURNAL NOTES

# CAMPSITE LOG

DATE(S): _____

**CAMP:** _____

**LOCATION:** _____

**DIRECTIONS:** _____

**STATE:** _____ **ALTITUDE:** _____ **GPS:** _____

**ROAD CONDITIONS:** _____

**CELL SIGNAL:** _____ **WIFI:** _____ **WEBSITE:** _____

**WEATHER:** _____ **NOISE:** _____ **MAXIMUM STAY:** _____

**PROS:** _____

**CONS:** _____

**TIPS FOR NEXT STAY:** _____

**NOTES:** _____

☆ ☆ ☆ ☆ ☆

## ON-SITE CAMP AMENITIES:

- ☐ Picnic Tables
- ☐ Hiking Trails
- ☐ Boat Dock
- ☐ Pit Toilet

- ☐ Fire Pit
- ☐ Water
- ☐ Shade
- ☐ Views

- ☐ Nature Reserve
- ☐ Historic Sites
- ☐ Fishing
- ☐ OHV Trails
- ☐ Other _____

## NEARBY AMENITIES & NECESSITIES:

**GAS:** _____ **PROPANE:** _____

**GROCERIES:** _____ **C-STORE:** _____

**DRINKING WATER:** _____ **NON-POTABLE WATER:** _____

**DUMP STATION:** _____ **DUMPSTER:** _____

**LAUNDRY:** _____ **SHOWERS:** _____

**FIREWOOD:** _____ **DOG PARK:** _____

**HIKING TRAILS:** _____

**ATTRACTIONS:** _____

**RANGER STATION:** _____

**OTHER:** _____

# IMAGES & JOURNAL NOTES

# CAMPSITE LOG

DATE(S): _____

**CAMP:** _____

**LOCATION:** _____

**DIRECTIONS:** _____

**STATE:** _____ **ALTITUDE:** _____ **GPS:** _____

**ROAD CONDITIONS:** _____

**CELL SIGNAL:** _____ **WIFI:** _____ **WEBSITE:** _____

**WEATHER:** _____ **NOISE:** _____ **MAXIMUM STAY:** _____

**PROS:** _____

**CONS:** _____

**TIPS FOR NEXT STAY:** _____

**NOTES:** _____

☆ ☆ ☆ ☆ ☆

## ON-SITE CAMP AMENITIES:

☐ Picnic Tables       ☐ Fire Pit       ☐ Nature Reserve

☐ Hiking Trails       ☐ Water          ☐ Historic Sites

☐ Boat Dock           ☐ Shade          ☐ Fishing

☐ Pit Toilet          ☐ Views          ☐ OHV Trails

                                       ☐ Other _____

## NEARBY AMENITIES & NECESSITIES:

**GAS:** _____        **PROPANE:** _____

**GROCERIES:** _____  **C-STORE:** _____

**DRINKING WATER:** _____  **NON-POTABLE WATER:** _____

**DUMP STATION:** _____  **DUMPSTER:** _____

**LAUNDRY:** _____  **SHOWERS:** _____

**FIREWOOD:** _____  **DOG PARK:** _____

**HIKING TRAILS:** _____

**ATTRACTIONS:** _____

**RANGER STATION:** _____

**OTHER:** _____

# IMAGES & JOURNAL NOTES

# CAMPSITE LOG

DATE(S): _____

**CAMP:** _____

**LOCATION:** _____

**DIRECTIONS:** _____

**STATE:** _____ **ALTITUDE:** _____ **GPS:** _____

**ROAD CONDITIONS:** _____

**CELL SIGNAL:** _____ **WIFI:** _____ **WEBSITE:** _____

**WEATHER:** _____ **NOISE:** _____ **MAXIMUM STAY:** _____

**PROS:** _____

**CONS:** _____

**TIPS FOR NEXT STAY:** _____

**NOTES:** _____

☆ ☆ ☆ ☆ ☆

## ON-SITE CAMP AMENITIES:

- ☐ Picnic Tables
- ☐ Hiking Trails
- ☐ Boat Dock
- ☐ Pit Toilet

- ☐ Fire Pit
- ☐ Water
- ☐ Shade
- ☐ Views

- ☐ Nature Reserve
- ☐ Historic Sites
- ☐ Fishing
- ☐ OHV Trails
- ☐ Other _____

## NEARBY AMENITIES & NECESSITIES:

**GAS:** _____ **PROPANE:** _____

**GROCERIES:** _____ **C-STORE:** _____

**DRINKING WATER:** _____ **NON-POTABLE WATER:** _____

**DUMP STATION:** _____ **DUMPSTER:** _____

**LAUNDRY:** _____ **SHOWERS:** _____

**FIREWOOD:** _____ **DOG PARK:** _____

**HIKING TRAILS:** _____

**ATTRACTIONS:** _____

**RANGER STATION:** _____

**OTHER:** _____

# IMAGES & JOURNAL NOTES

# CAMPSITE LOG

DATE(S): _____

**CAMP:** _____

**LOCATION:** _____

DIRECTIONS: _____

STATE: _____ ALTITUDE: _____ GPS: _____

ROAD CONDITIONS: _____

CELL SIGNAL: _____ WIFI: _____ WEBSITE: _____

WEATHER: _____ NOISE: _____ MAXIMUM STAY: _____

PROS: _____

CONS: _____

TIPS FOR NEXT STAY: _____

NOTES: _____

☆ ☆ ☆ ☆ ☆

## ON-SITE CAMP AMENITIES:

☐ Picnic Tables          ☐ Fire Pit          ☐ Nature Reserve
☐ Hiking Trails          ☐ Water             ☐ Historic Sites
☐ Boat Dock              ☐ Shade             ☐ Fishing
☐ Pit Toilet             ☐ Views             ☐ OHV Trails
                                             ☐ Other _____

## NEARBY AMENITIES & NECESSITIES:

GAS: _____                    PROPANE: _____

GROCERIES: _____              C-STORE: _____

DRINKING WATER: _____         NON-POTABLE WATER: _____

DUMP STATION: _____           DUMPSTER: _____

LAUNDRY: _____                SHOWERS: _____

FIREWOOD: _____               DOG PARK: _____

HIKING TRAILS: _____

ATTRACTIONS: _____

RANGER STATION: _____

OTHER: _____

# IMAGES & JOURNAL NOTES

# CAMPSITE LOG

DATE(S): _____

CAMP: _____

LOCATION: _____

DIRECTIONS: _____

STATE: _____ ALTITUDE: _____ GPS: _____

ROAD CONDITIONS: _____

CELL SIGNAL: _____ WIFI: _____ WEBSITE: _____

WEATHER: _____ NOISE: _____ MAXIMUM STAY: _____

PROS: _____

CONS: _____

TIPS FOR NEXT STAY: _____

NOTES: _____

☆ ☆ ☆ ☆ ☆

## ON-SITE CAMP AMENITIES:

- ☐ Picnic Tables
- ☐ Hiking Trails
- ☐ Boat Dock
- ☐ Pit Toilet
- ☐ Fire Pit
- ☐ Water
- ☐ Shade
- ☐ Views
- ☐ Nature Reserve
- ☐ Historic Sites
- ☐ Fishing
- ☐ OHV Trails
- ☐ Other _____

## NEARBY AMENITIES & NECESSITIES:

GAS: _____ PROPANE: _____

GROCERIES: _____ C-STORE: _____

DRINKING WATER: _____ NON-POTABLE WATER: _____

DUMP STATION: _____ DUMPSTER: _____

LAUNDRY: _____ SHOWERS: _____

FIREWOOD: _____ DOG PARK: _____

HIKING TRAILS: _____

ATTRACTIONS: _____

RANGER STATION: _____

OTHER: _____

# IMAGES & JOURNAL NOTES

# CAMPSITE LOG

DATE(S): _____

**CAMP:** _____

**LOCATION:** _____

**DIRECTIONS:** _____

**STATE:** _____ **ALTITUDE:** _____ **GPS:** _____

**ROAD CONDITIONS:** _____

**CELL SIGNAL:** _____ **WIFI:** _____ **WEBSITE:** _____

**WEATHER:** _____ **NOISE:** _____ **MAXIMUM STAY:** _____

**PROS:** _____

**CONS:** _____

**TIPS FOR NEXT STAY:** _____

**NOTES:** _____

☆ ☆ ☆ ☆ ☆

## ON-SITE CAMP AMENITIES:

- ☐ Picnic Tables
- ☐ Hiking Trails
- ☐ Boat Dock
- ☐ Pit Toilet
- ☐ Fire Pit
- ☐ Water
- ☐ Shade
- ☐ Views
- ☐ Nature Reserve
- ☐ Historic Sites
- ☐ Fishing
- ☐ OHV Trails
- ☐ Other _____

## NEARBY AMENITIES & NECESSITIES:

**GAS:** _____ **PROPANE:** _____

**GROCERIES:** _____ **C-STORE:** _____

**DRINKING WATER:** _____ **NON-POTABLE WATER:** _____

**DUMP STATION:** _____ **DUMPSTER:** _____

**LAUNDRY:** _____ **SHOWERS:** _____

**FIREWOOD:** _____ **DOG PARK:** _____

**HIKING TRAILS:** _____

**ATTRACTIONS:** _____

**RANGER STATION:** _____

**OTHER:** _____

# IMAGES & JOURNAL NOTES

# CAMPSITE LOG

DATE(S): _____

**CAMP:** _____

**LOCATION:** _____

DIRECTIONS: _____

STATE: _____ ALTITUDE: _____ GPS: _____

ROAD CONDITIONS: _____

CELL SIGNAL: _____ WIFI: _____ WEBSITE: _____

WEATHER: _____ NOISE: _____ MAXIMUM STAY: _____

PROS: _____

CONS: _____

TIPS FOR NEXT STAY: _____

NOTES: _____

_____

☆ ☆ ☆ ☆ ☆

## ON-SITE CAMP AMENITIES:

- ☐ Picnic Tables
- ☐ Hiking Trails
- ☐ Boat Dock
- ☐ Pit Toilet
- ☐ Fire Pit
- ☐ Water
- ☐ Shade
- ☐ Views
- ☐ Nature Reserve
- ☐ Historic Sites
- ☐ Fishing
- ☐ OHV Trails
- ☐ Other _____

## NEARBY AMENITIES & NECESSITIES:

GAS: _____ PROPANE: _____

GROCERIES: _____ C-STORE: _____

DRINKING WATER: _____ NON-POTABLE WATER: _____

DUMP STATION: _____ DUMPSTER: _____

LAUNDRY: _____ SHOWERS: _____

FIREWOOD: _____ DOG PARK: _____

HIKING TRAILS: _____

ATTRACTIONS: _____

RANGER STATION: _____

OTHER: _____

_____

# IMAGES & JOURNAL NOTES

# CAMPSITE LOG

DATE(S): _____

CAMP: _____

LOCATION: _____

DIRECTIONS: _____

STATE: _____ ALTITUDE: _____ GPS: _____

ROAD CONDITIONS: _____

CELL SIGNAL: _____ WIFI: _____ WEBSITE: _____

WEATHER: _____ NOISE: _____ MAXIMUM STAY: _____

PROS: _____

CONS: _____

TIPS FOR NEXT STAY: _____

NOTES: _____

☆ ☆ ☆ ☆ ☆

## ON-SITE CAMP AMENITIES:

☐ Nature Reserve

☐ Picnic Tables ☐ Fire Pit ☐ Historic Sites

☐ Hiking Trails ☐ Water ☐ Fishing

☐ Boat Dock ☐ Shade ☐ OHV Trails

☐ Pit Toilet ☐ Views ☐ Other _____

## NEARBY AMENITIES & NECESSITIES:

GAS: _____ PROPANE: _____

GROCERIES: _____ C-STORE: _____

DRINKING WATER: _____ NON-POTABLE WATER: _____

DUMP STATION: _____ DUMPSTER: _____

LAUNDRY: _____ SHOWERS: _____

FIREWOOD: _____ DOG PARK: _____

HIKING TRAILS: _____

ATTRACTIONS: _____

RANGER STATION: _____

OTHER: _____

# IMAGES & JOURNAL NOTES

# CAMPSITE LOG

DATE(S): _____

CAMP: _____

LOCATION: _____

DIRECTIONS: _____

STATE: _____ ALTITUDE: _____ GPS: _____

ROAD CONDITIONS: _____

CELL SIGNAL: _____ WIFI: _____ WEBSITE: _____

WEATHER: _____ NOISE: _____ MAXIMUM STAY: _____

PROS: _____

CONS: _____

TIPS FOR NEXT STAY: _____

NOTES: _____

☆☆☆☆☆

## ON-SITE CAMP AMENITIES:

- ☐ Picnic Tables
- ☐ Hiking Trails
- ☐ Boat Dock
- ☐ Pit Toilet

- ☐ Fire Pit
- ☐ Water
- ☐ Shade
- ☐ Views

- ☐ Nature Reserve
- ☐ Historic Sites
- ☐ Fishing
- ☐ OHV Trails
- ☐ Other _____

## NEARBY AMENITIES & NECESSITIES:

GAS: _____ PROPANE: _____

GROCERIES: _____ C-STORE: _____

DRINKING WATER: _____ NON-POTABLE WATER: _____

DUMP STATION: _____ DUMPSTER: _____

LAUNDRY: _____ SHOWERS: _____

FIREWOOD: _____ DOG PARK: _____

HIKING TRAILS: _____

ATTRACTIONS: _____

RANGER STATION: _____

OTHER: _____

# IMAGES & JOURNAL NOTES

# CAMPSITE LOG

DATE(S): _____

CAMP: _____

LOCATION: _____

DIRECTIONS: _____

STATE: _____ ALTITUDE: _____ GPS: _____

ROAD CONDITIONS: _____

CELL SIGNAL: _____ WIFI: _____ WEBSITE: _____

WEATHER: _____ NOISE: _____ MAXIMUM STAY: _____

PROS: _____

CONS: _____

TIPS FOR NEXT STAY: _____

NOTES: _____

☆ ☆ ☆ ☆ ☆

## ON-SITE CAMP AMENITIES:

- ☐ Picnic Tables
- ☐ Hiking Trails
- ☐ Boat Dock
- ☐ Pit Toilet

- ☐ Fire Pit
- ☐ Water
- ☐ Shade
- ☐ Views

- ☐ Nature Reserve
- ☐ Historic Sites
- ☐ Fishing
- ☐ OHV Trails
- ☐ Other _____

## NEARBY AMENITIES & NECESSITIES:

GAS: _____ PROPANE: _____

GROCERIES: _____ C-STORE: _____

DRINKING WATER: _____ NON-POTABLE WATER: _____

DUMP STATION: _____ DUMPSTER: _____

LAUNDRY: _____ SHOWERS: _____

FIREWOOD: _____ DOG PARK: _____

HIKING TRAILS: _____

ATTRACTIONS: _____

RANGER STATION: _____

OTHER: _____

# IMAGES & JOURNAL NOTES

# CAMPSITE LOG

DATE(S): _____

**CAMP:** _____

**LOCATION:** _____

**DIRECTIONS:** _____

**STATE:** _____ **ALTITUDE:** _____ **GPS:** _____

**ROAD CONDITIONS:** _____

**CELL SIGNAL:** _____ **WIFI:** _____ **WEBSITE:** _____

**WEATHER:** _____ **NOISE:** _____ **MAXIMUM STAY:** _____

**PROS:** _____

**CONS:** _____

**TIPS FOR NEXT STAY:** _____

**NOTES:** _____

☆ ☆ ☆ ☆ ☆

## ON-SITE CAMP AMENITIES:

- ☐ Picnic Tables
- ☐ Hiking Trails
- ☐ Boat Dock
- ☐ Pit Toilet

- ☐ Fire Pit
- ☐ Water
- ☐ Shade
- ☐ Views

- ☐ Nature Reserve
- ☐ Historic Sites
- ☐ Fishing
- ☐ OHV Trails
- ☐ Other _____

## NEARBY AMENITIES & NECESSITIES:

**GAS:** _____

**PROPANE:** _____

**GROCERIES:** _____

**C-STORE:** _____

**DRINKING WATER:** _____

**NON-POTABLE WATER:** _____

**DUMP STATION:** _____

**DUMPSTER:** _____

**LAUNDRY:** _____

**SHOWERS:** _____

**FIREWOOD:** _____

**DOG PARK:** _____

**HIKING TRAILS:** _____

**ATTRACTIONS:** _____

**RANGER STATION:** _____

**OTHER:** _____

# IMAGES & JOURNAL NOTES

# CAMPSITE LOG

DATE(S): _____

**CAMP:** _____

**LOCATION:** _____

**DIRECTIONS:** _____

**STATE:** _____ **ALTITUDE:** _____ **GPS:** _____

**ROAD CONDITIONS:** _____

**CELL SIGNAL:** _____ **WIFI:** _____ **WEBSITE:** _____

**WEATHER:** _____ **NOISE:** _____ **MAXIMUM STAY:** _____

**PROS:** _____

**CONS:** _____

**TIPS FOR NEXT STAY:** _____

**NOTES:** _____

☆ ☆ ☆ ☆ ☆

## ON-SITE CAMP AMENITIES:

- ☐ Picnic Tables
- ☐ Hiking Trails
- ☐ Boat Dock
- ☐ Pit Toilet
- ☐ Fire Pit
- ☐ Water
- ☐ Shade
- ☐ Views
- ☐ Nature Reserve
- ☐ Historic Sites
- ☐ Fishing
- ☐ OHV Trails
- ☐ Other _____

## NEARBY AMENITIES & NECESSITIES:

**GAS:** _____ **PROPANE:** _____

**GROCERIES:** _____ **C-STORE:** _____

**DRINKING WATER:** _____ **NON-POTABLE WATER:** _____

**DUMP STATION:** _____ **DUMPSTER:** _____

**LAUNDRY:** _____ **SHOWERS:** _____

**FIREWOOD:** _____ **DOG PARK:** _____

**HIKING TRAILS:** _____

**ATTRACTIONS:** _____

**RANGER STATION:** _____

**OTHER:** _____

# IMAGES & JOURNAL NOTES

# CAMPSITE LOG

DATE(S): _____

CAMP: _____

LOCATION: _____

DIRECTIONS: _____

STATE: _____ ALTITUDE: _____ GPS: _____

ROAD CONDITIONS: _____

CELL SIGNAL: _____ WIFI: _____ WEBSITE: _____

WEATHER: _____ NOISE: _____ MAXIMUM STAY: _____

PROS: _____

CONS: _____

TIPS FOR NEXT STAY: _____

NOTES: _____

☆ ☆ ☆ ☆ ☆

## ON-SITE CAMP AMENITIES:

☐ Nature Reserve

☐ Picnic Tables    ☐ Fire Pit    ☐ Historic Sites

☐ Hiking Trails    ☐ Water    ☐ Fishing

☐ Boat Dock    ☐ Shade    ☐ OHV Trails

☐ Pit Toilet    ☐ Views    ☐ Other _____

## NEARBY AMENITIES & NECESSITIES:

GAS: _____ PROPANE: _____

GROCERIES: _____ C-STORE: _____

DRINKING WATER: _____ NON-POTABLE WATER: _____

DUMP STATION: _____ DUMPSTER: _____

LAUNDRY: _____ SHOWERS: _____

FIREWOOD: _____ DOG PARK: _____

HIKING TRAILS: _____

ATTRACTIONS: _____

RANGER STATION: _____

OTHER: _____

# IMAGES & JOURNAL NOTES

# CAMPSITE LOG

DATE(S): _____

CAMP: _____

LOCATION: _____

DIRECTIONS: _____

STATE: _____ ALTITUDE: _____ GPS: _____

ROAD CONDITIONS: _____

CELL SIGNAL: _____ WIFI: _____ WEBSITE: _____

WEATHER: _____ NOISE: _____ MAXIMUM STAY: _____

PROS: _____

CONS: _____

TIPS FOR NEXT STAY: _____

NOTES: _____

☆ ☆ ☆ ☆ ☆

## ON-SITE CAMP AMENITIES:

☐ Picnic Tables       ☐ Fire Pit       ☐ Nature Reserve
☐ Hiking Trails       ☐ Water          ☐ Historic Sites
☐ Boat Dock           ☐ Shade          ☐ Fishing
☐ Pit Toilet          ☐ Views          ☐ OHV Trails
                                        ☐ Other _____

## NEARBY AMENITIES & NECESSITIES:

GAS: _____          PROPANE: _____

GROCERIES: _____          C-STORE: _____

DRINKING WATER: ____          NON-POTABLE WATER: _____

DUMP STATION: _____          DUMPSTER: _____

LAUNDRY: _____          SHOWERS: _____

FIREWOOD: _____          DOG PARK: _____

HIKING TRAILS: _____

ATTRACTIONS: _____

RANGER STATION: _____

OTHER: _____

# IMAGES & JOURNAL NOTES

# CAMPSITE LOG

DATE(S): _____

CAMP: _____

LOCATION: _____

DIRECTIONS: _____

STATE: _____ ALTITUDE: _____ GPS: _____

ROAD CONDITIONS: _____

CELL SIGNAL: _____ WIFI: _____ WEBSITE: _____

WEATHER: _____ NOISE: _____ MAXIMUM STAY: _____

PROS: _____

CONS: _____

TIPS FOR NEXT STAY: _____

NOTES: _____

☆ ☆ ☆ ☆ ☆

## ON-SITE CAMP AMENITIES:

- ☐ Picnic Tables
- ☐ Hiking Trails
- ☐ Boat Dock
- ☐ Pit Toilet

- ☐ Fire Pit
- ☐ Water
- ☐ Shade
- ☐ Views

- ☐ Nature Reserve
- ☐ Historic Sites
- ☐ Fishing
- ☐ OHV Trails
- ☐ Other _____

## NEARBY AMENITIES & NECESSITIES:

GAS: _____ | PROPANE: _____

GROCERIES: _____ | C-STORE: _____

DRINKING WATER: _____ | NON-POTABLE WATER: _____

DUMP STATION: _____ | DUMPSTER: _____

LAUNDRY: _____ | SHOWERS: _____

FIREWOOD: _____ | DOG PARK: _____

HIKING TRAILS: _____

ATTRACTIONS: _____

RANGER STATION: _____

OTHER: _____

# IMAGES & JOURNAL NOTES

# CAMPSITE LOG

DATE(S): _____

**CAMP:** _____

**LOCATION:** _____

**DIRECTIONS:** _____

**STATE:** _____ **ALTITUDE:** _____ **GPS:** _____

**ROAD CONDITIONS:** _____

**CELL SIGNAL:** _____ **WIFI:** _____ **WEBSITE:** _____

**WEATHER:** _____ **NOISE:** _____ **MAXIMUM STAY:** _____

**PROS:** _____

**CONS:** _____

**TIPS FOR NEXT STAY:** _____

**NOTES:** _____

☆ ☆ ☆ ☆ ☆

## ON-SITE CAMP AMENITIES:

☐ Picnic Tables    ☐ Fire Pit    ☐ Nature Reserve
☐ Hiking Trails    ☐ Water    ☐ Historic Sites
☐ Boat Dock    ☐ Shade    ☐ Fishing
☐ Pit Toilet    ☐ Views    ☐ OHV Trails
   ☐ Other _____

## NEARBY AMENITIES & NECESSITIES:

**GAS:** _____ **PROPANE:** _____

**GROCERIES:** _____ **C-STORE:** _____

**DRINKING WATER:** _____ **NON-POTABLE WATER:** _____

**DUMP STATION:** _____ **DUMPSTER:** _____

**LAUNDRY:** _____ **SHOWERS:** _____

**FIREWOOD:** _____ **DOG PARK:** _____

**HIKING TRAILS:** _____

**ATTRACTIONS:** _____

**RANGER STATION:** _____

**OTHER:** _____

# IMAGES & JOURNAL NOTES

# CAMPSITE LOG

DATE(S): _____

**CAMP:** _____

**LOCATION:** _____

**DIRECTIONS:** _____

**STATE:** _____ **ALTITUDE:** _____ **GPS:** _____

**ROAD CONDITIONS:** _____

**CELL SIGNAL:** _____ **WIFI:** _____ **WEBSITE:** _____

**WEATHER:** _____ **NOISE:** _____ **MAXIMUM STAY:** _____

**PROS:** _____

**CONS:** _____

**TIPS FOR NEXT STAY:** _____

**NOTES:** _____

☆ ☆ ☆ ☆ ☆

## ON-SITE CAMP AMENITIES:

☐ Picnic Tables    ☐ Fire Pit    ☐ Nature Reserve

☐ Hiking Trails    ☐ Water    ☐ Historic Sites

☐ Boat Dock    ☐ Shade    ☐ Fishing

☐ Pit Toilet    ☐ Views    ☐ OHV Trails

☐ Other _____

## NEARBY AMENITIES & NECESSITIES:

**GAS:** _____ **PROPANE:** _____

**GROCERIES:** _____ **C-STORE:** _____

**DRINKING WATER:** _____ **NON-POTABLE WATER:** _____

**DUMP STATION:** _____ **DUMPSTER:** _____

**LAUNDRY:** _____ **SHOWERS:** _____

**FIREWOOD:** _____ **DOG PARK:** _____

**HIKING TRAILS:** _____

**ATTRACTIONS:** _____

**RANGER STATION:** _____

**OTHER:** _____

# IMAGES & JOURNAL NOTES

# CAMPSITE LOG

DATE(S): _____

**CAMP:** _____

**LOCATION:** _____

**DIRECTIONS:** _____

**STATE:** _____ **ALTITUDE:** _____ **GPS:** _____

**ROAD CONDITIONS:** _____

**CELL SIGNAL:** _____ **WIFI:** _____ **WEBSITE:** _____

**WEATHER:** _____ **NOISE:** _____ **MAXIMUM STAY:** _____

**PROS:** _____

**CONS:** _____

**TIPS FOR NEXT STAY:** _____

**NOTES:** _____

☆ ☆ ☆ ☆ ☆

## ON-SITE CAMP AMENITIES:

- ☐ Picnic Tables
- ☐ Hiking Trails
- ☐ Boat Dock
- ☐ Pit Toilet
- ☐ Fire Pit
- ☐ Water
- ☐ Shade
- ☐ Views
- ☐ Nature Reserve
- ☐ Historic Sites
- ☐ Fishing
- ☐ OHV Trails
- ☐ Other _____

## NEARBY AMENITIES & NECESSITIES:

**GAS:** _____ **PROPANE:** _____

**GROCERIES:** _____ **C-STORE:** _____

**DRINKING WATER:** _____ **NON-POTABLE WATER:** _____

**DUMP STATION:** _____ **DUMPSTER:** _____

**LAUNDRY:** _____ **SHOWERS:** _____

**FIREWOOD:** _____ **DOG PARK:** _____

**HIKING TRAILS:** _____

**ATTRACTIONS:** _____

**RANGER STATION:** _____

**OTHER:** _____

# IMAGES & JOURNAL NOTES

# CAMPSITE LOG

DATE(S): _____

CAMP: _____

LOCATION: _____

DIRECTIONS: _____

STATE: _____ ALTITUDE: _____ GPS: _____

ROAD CONDITIONS: _____

CELL SIGNAL: _____ WIFI: _____ WEBSITE: _____

WEATHER: _____ NOISE: _____ MAXIMUM STAY: _____

PROS: _____

CONS: _____

TIPS FOR NEXT STAY: _____

NOTES: _____

☆ ☆ ☆ ☆ ☆

## ON-SITE CAMP AMENITIES:

- ☐ Picnic Tables
- ☐ Hiking Trails
- ☐ Boat Dock
- ☐ Pit Toilet

- ☐ Fire Pit
- ☐ Water
- ☐ Shade
- ☐ Views

- ☐ Nature Reserve
- ☐ Historic Sites
- ☐ Fishing
- ☐ OHV Trails
- ☐ Other _____

## NEARBY AMENITIES & NECESSITIES:

GAS: _____ PROPANE: _____

GROCERIES: _____ C-STORE: _____

DRINKING WATER: _____ NON-POTABLE WATER: _____

DUMP STATION: _____ DUMPSTER: _____

LAUNDRY: _____ SHOWERS: _____

FIREWOOD: _____ DOG PARK: _____

HIKING TRAILS: _____

ATTRACTIONS: _____

RANGER STATION: _____

OTHER: _____

# IMAGES & JOURNAL NOTES

# CAMPSITE LOG

DATE(S): _____

**CAMP:** _____

**LOCATION:** _____

**DIRECTIONS:** _____

**STATE:** _____ **ALTITUDE:** _____ **GPS:** _____

**ROAD CONDITIONS:** _____

**CELL SIGNAL:** _____ **WIFI:** _____ **WEBSITE:** _____

**WEATHER:** _____ **NOISE:** _____ **MAXIMUM STAY:** _____

**PROS:** _____

**CONS:** _____

**TIPS FOR NEXT STAY:** _____

**NOTES:** _____

☆ ☆ ☆ ☆ ☆

## ON-SITE CAMP AMENITIES:

☐ Picnic Tables          ☐ Fire Pit          ☐ Nature Reserve

☐ Hiking Trails          ☐ Water             ☐ Historic Sites

☐ Boat Dock              ☐ Shade             ☐ Fishing

☐ Pit Toilet             ☐ Views             ☐ OHV Trails

                                              ☐ Other _____

## NEARBY AMENITIES & NECESSITIES:

**GAS:** _____                   **PROPANE:** _____

**GROCERIES:** _____             **C-STORE:** _____

**DRINKING WATER:** _____        **NON-POTABLE WATER:** _____

**DUMP STATION:** _____          **DUMPSTER:** _____

**LAUNDRY:** _____               **SHOWERS:** _____

**FIREWOOD:** _____              **DOG PARK:** _____

**HIKING TRAILS:** _____

**ATTRACTIONS:** _____

**RANGER STATION:** _____

**OTHER:** _____

# IMAGES & JOURNAL NOTES

# CAMPSITE LOG

DATE(S): _____

CAMP: _____

LOCATION: _____

DIRECTIONS: _____

STATE: _____ ALTITUDE: _____ GPS: _____

ROAD CONDITIONS: _____

CELL SIGNAL: _____ WIFI: _____ WEBSITE: _____

WEATHER: _____ NOISE: _____ MAXIMUM STAY: _____

PROS: _____

CONS: _____

TIPS FOR NEXT STAY: _____

NOTES: _____

☆ ☆ ☆ ☆ ☆

## ON-SITE CAMP AMENITIES:

- ☐ Picnic Tables
- ☐ Hiking Trails
- ☐ Boat Dock
- ☐ Pit Toilet

- ☐ Fire Pit
- ☐ Water
- ☐ Shade
- ☐ Views

- ☐ Nature Reserve
- ☐ Historic Sites
- ☐ Fishing
- ☐ OHV Trails
- ☐ Other _____

## NEARBY AMENITIES & NECESSITIES:

GAS: _____

PROPANE: _____

GROCERIES: _____

C-STORE: _____

DRINKING WATER: _____

NON-POTABLE WATER: _____

DUMP STATION: _____

DUMPSTER: _____

LAUNDRY: _____

SHOWERS: _____

FIREWOOD: _____

DOG PARK: _____

HIKING TRAILS: _____

ATTRACTIONS: _____

RANGER STATION: _____

OTHER: _____

# IMAGES & JOURNAL NOTES

# CAMPSITE LOG

DATE(S): _____

CAMP: _____

LOCATION: _____

DIRECTIONS: _____

STATE: _____ ALTITUDE: _____ GPS: _____

ROAD CONDITIONS: _____

CELL SIGNAL: _____ WIFI: _____ WEBSITE: _____

WEATHER: _____ NOISE: _____ MAXIMUM STAY: _____

PROS: _____

CONS: _____

TIPS FOR NEXT STAY: _____

NOTES: _____

☆ ☆ ☆ ☆ ☆

## ON-SITE CAMP AMENITIES:

☐ Picnic Tables     ☐ Fire Pit     ☐ Nature Reserve
☐ Hiking Trails     ☐ Water        ☐ Historic Sites
☐ Boat Dock         ☐ Shade        ☐ Fishing
☐ Pit Toilet        ☐ Views        ☐ OHV Trails
                                   ☐ Other _____

## NEARBY AMENITIES & NECESSITIES:

GAS: _____ PROPANE: _____

GROCERIES: _____ C-STORE: _____

DRINKING WATER: _____ NON-POTABLE WATER: _____

DUMP STATION: _____ DUMPSTER: _____

LAUNDRY: _____ SHOWERS: _____

FIREWOOD: _____ DOG PARK: _____

HIKING TRAILS: _____

ATTRACTIONS: _____

RANGER STATION: _____

OTHER: _____

# IMAGES & JOURNAL NOTES

# CAMPSITE LOG

DATE(S): _____

**CAMP:** _____

**LOCATION:** _____

**DIRECTIONS:** _____

**STATE:** _____ **ALTITUDE:** _____ **GPS:** _____

**ROAD CONDITIONS:** _____

**CELL SIGNAL:** _____ **WIFI:** _____ **WEBSITE:** _____

**WEATHER:** _____ **NOISE:** _____ **MAXIMUM STAY:** _____

**PROS:** _____

**CONS:** _____

**TIPS FOR NEXT STAY:** _____

**NOTES:** _____

_____

☆ ☆ ☆ ☆ ☆

## ON-SITE CAMP AMENITIES:

- ☐ Picnic Tables
- ☐ Hiking Trails
- ☐ Boat Dock
- ☐ Pit Toilet

- ☐ Fire Pit
- ☐ Water
- ☐ Shade
- ☐ Views

- ☐ Nature Reserve
- ☐ Historic Sites
- ☐ Fishing
- ☐ OHV Trails
- ☐ Other _____

## NEARBY AMENITIES & NECESSITIES:

**GAS:** _____  **PROPANE:** _____

**GROCERIES:** _____  **C-STORE:** _____

**DRINKING WATER:** _____  **NON-POTABLE WATER:** _____

**DUMP STATION:** _____  **DUMPSTER:** _____

**LAUNDRY:** _____  **SHOWERS:** _____

**FIREWOOD:** _____  **DOG PARK:** _____

**HIKING TRAILS:** _____

**ATTRACTIONS:** _____

**RANGER STATION:** _____

**OTHER:** _____

# IMAGES & JOURNAL NOTES

# CAMPSITE LOG

DATE(S): _____

**CAMP:** _____

**LOCATION:** _____

**DIRECTIONS:** _____

**STATE:** _____ **ALTITUDE:** _____ **GPS:** _____

**ROAD CONDITIONS:** _____

**CELL SIGNAL:** _____ **WIFI:** _____ **WEBSITE:** _____

**WEATHER:** _____ **NOISE:** _____ **MAXIMUM STAY:** _____

**PROS:** _____

**CONS:** _____

**TIPS FOR NEXT STAY:** _____

**NOTES:** _____

☆ ☆ ☆ ☆ ☆

## ON-SITE CAMP AMENITIES:

☐ Picnic Tables      ☐ Fire Pit      ☐ Nature Reserve
☐ Hiking Trails      ☐ Water      ☐ Historic Sites
☐ Boat Dock      ☐ Shade      ☐ Fishing
☐ Pit Toilet      ☐ Views      ☐ OHV Trails
                          ☐ Other _____

## NEARBY AMENITIES & NECESSITIES:

**GAS:** _____ **PROPANE:** _____

**GROCERIES:** _____ **C-STORE:** _____

**DRINKING WATER:** _____ **NON-POTABLE WATER:** _____

**DUMP STATION:** _____ **DUMPSTER:** _____

**LAUNDRY:** _____ **SHOWERS:** _____

**FIREWOOD:** _____ **DOG PARK:** _____

**HIKING TRAILS:** _____

**ATTRACTIONS:** _____

**RANGER STATION:** _____

**OTHER:** _____

# IMAGES & JOURNAL NOTES

# CAMPSITE LOG

DATE(S): _____

**CAMP:** _____

**LOCATION:** _____

**DIRECTIONS:** _____

**STATE:** _____ **ALTITUDE:** _____ **GPS:** _____

**ROAD CONDITIONS:** _____

**CELL SIGNAL:** _____ **WIFI:** _____ **WEBSITE:** _____

**WEATHER:** _____ **NOISE:** _____ **MAXIMUM STAY:** _____

**PROS:** _____

**CONS:** _____

**TIPS FOR NEXT STAY:** _____

**NOTES:** _____

☆ ☆ ☆ ☆ ☆

## ON-SITE CAMP AMENITIES:

- ☐ Picnic Tables
- ☐ Hiking Trails
- ☐ Boat Dock
- ☐ Pit Toilet

- ☐ Fire Pit
- ☐ Water
- ☐ Shade
- ☐ Views

- ☐ Nature Reserve
- ☐ Historic Sites
- ☐ Fishing
- ☐ OHV Trails
- ☐ Other _____

## NEARBY AMENITIES & NECESSITIES:

**GAS:** _____  **PROPANE:** _____

**GROCERIES:** _____  **C-STORE:** _____

**DRINKING WATER:** _____  **NON-POTABLE WATER:** _____

**DUMP STATION:** _____  **DUMPSTER:** _____

**LAUNDRY:** _____  **SHOWERS:** _____

**FIREWOOD:** _____  **DOG PARK:** _____

**HIKING TRAILS:** _____

**ATTRACTIONS:** _____

**RANGER STATION:** _____

**OTHER:** _____

# IMAGES & JOURNAL NOTES

# CAMPSITE LOG

DATE(S): _____

**CAMP:** _____

**LOCATION:** _____

**DIRECTIONS:** _____

**STATE:** _____ **ALTITUDE:** _____ **GPS:** _____

**ROAD CONDITIONS:** _____

**CELL SIGNAL:** _____ **WIFI:** _____ **WEBSITE:** _____

**WEATHER:** _____ **NOISE:** _____ **MAXIMUM STAY:** _____

**PROS:** _____

**CONS:** _____

**TIPS FOR NEXT STAY:** _____

**NOTES:** _____

☆ ☆ ☆ ☆ ☆

## ON-SITE CAMP AMENITIES:

- ☐ Picnic Tables
- ☐ Hiking Trails
- ☐ Boat Dock
- ☐ Pit Toilet

- ☐ Fire Pit
- ☐ Water
- ☐ Shade
- ☐ Views

- ☐ Nature Reserve
- ☐ Historic Sites
- ☐ Fishing
- ☐ OHV Trails
- ☐ Other _____

## NEARBY AMENITIES & NECESSITIES:

**GAS:** _____ **PROPANE:** _____

**GROCERIES:** _____ **C-STORE:** _____

**DRINKING WATER:** _____ **NON-POTABLE WATER:** _____

**DUMP STATION:** _____ **DUMPSTER:** _____

**LAUNDRY:** _____ **SHOWERS:** _____

**FIREWOOD:** _____ **DOG PARK:** _____

**HIKING TRAILS:** _____

**ATTRACTIONS:** _____

**RANGER STATION:** _____

**OTHER:** _____

# IMAGES & JOURNAL NOTES

# CAMPSITE LOG

DATE(S): _____

**CAMP:** _____

**LOCATION:** _____

**DIRECTIONS:** _____

**STATE:** _____ **ALTITUDE:** _____ **GPS:** _____

**ROAD CONDITIONS:** _____

**CELL SIGNAL:** _____ **WIFI:** _____ **WEBSITE:** _____

**WEATHER:** _____ **NOISE:** _____ **MAXIMUM STAY:** _____

**PROS:** _____

**CONS:** _____

**TIPS FOR NEXT STAY:** _____

**NOTES:** _____

☆ ☆ ☆ ☆ ☆

## ON-SITE CAMP AMENITIES:

- ☐ Picnic Tables
- ☐ Hiking Trails
- ☐ Boat Dock
- ☐ Pit Toilet

- ☐ Fire Pit
- ☐ Water
- ☐ Shade
- ☐ Views

- ☐ Nature Reserve
- ☐ Historic Sites
- ☐ Fishing
- ☐ OHV Trails
- ☐ Other _____

## NEARBY AMENITIES & NECESSITIES:

**GAS:** _____ **PROPANE:** _____

**GROCERIES:** _____ **C-STORE:** _____

**DRINKING WATER:** _____ **NON-POTABLE WATER:** _____

**DUMP STATION:** _____ **DUMPSTER:** _____

**LAUNDRY:** _____ **SHOWERS:** _____

**FIREWOOD:** _____ **DOG PARK:** _____

**HIKING TRAILS:** _____

**ATTRACTIONS:** _____

**RANGER STATION:** _____

**OTHER:** _____

# IMAGES & JOURNAL NOTES

# CAMPSITE LOG

DATE(S): _____

CAMP: _____

LOCATION: _____

DIRECTIONS: _____

STATE: _____ ALTITUDE: _____ GPS: _____

ROAD CONDITIONS: _____

CELL SIGNAL: _____ WIFI: _____ WEBSITE: _____

WEATHER: _____ NOISE: _____ MAXIMUM STAY: _____

PROS: _____

CONS: _____

TIPS FOR NEXT STAY: _____

NOTES: _____

☆ ☆ ☆ ☆ ☆

## ON-SITE CAMP AMENITIES:

- ☐ Picnic Tables
- ☐ Hiking Trails
- ☐ Boat Dock
- ☐ Pit Toilet

- ☐ Fire Pit
- ☐ Water
- ☐ Shade
- ☐ Views

- ☐ Nature Reserve
- ☐ Historic Sites
- ☐ Fishing
- ☐ OHV Trails
- ☐ Other _____

## NEARBY AMENITIES & NECESSITIES:

GAS: _____  PROPANE: _____

GROCERIES: _____  C-STORE: _____

DRINKING WATER: _____  NON-POTABLE WATER: _____

DUMP STATION: _____  DUMPSTER: _____

LAUNDRY: _____  SHOWERS: _____

FIREWOOD: _____  DOG PARK: _____

HIKING TRAILS: _____

ATTRACTIONS: _____

RANGER STATION: _____

OTHER: _____

# IMAGES & JOURNAL NOTES

# CAMPSITE LOG

DATE(S): _____

**CAMP:** _____

**LOCATION:** _____

**DIRECTIONS:** _____

**STATE:** _____ **ALTITUDE:** _____ **GPS:** _____

**ROAD CONDITIONS:** _____

**CELL SIGNAL:** _____ **WIFI:** _____ **WEBSITE:** _____

**WEATHER:** _____ **NOISE:** _____ **MAXIMUM STAY:** _____

**PROS:** _____

**CONS:** _____

**TIPS FOR NEXT STAY:** _____

**NOTES:** _____

☆ ☆ ☆ ☆ ☆

## ON-SITE CAMP AMENITIES:

- ☐ Picnic Tables
- ☐ Hiking Trails
- ☐ Boat Dock
- ☐ Pit Toilet

- ☐ Fire Pit
- ☐ Water
- ☐ Shade
- ☐ Views

- ☐ Nature Reserve
- ☐ Historic Sites
- ☐ Fishing
- ☐ OHV Trails
- ☐ Other _____

## NEARBY AMENITIES & NECESSITIES:

**GAS:** _____ **PROPANE:** _____

**GROCERIES:** _____ **C-STORE:** _____

**DRINKING WATER:** _____ **NON-POTABLE WATER:** _____

**DUMP STATION:** _____ **DUMPSTER:** _____

**LAUNDRY:** _____ **SHOWERS:** _____

**FIREWOOD:** _____ **DOG PARK:** _____

**HIKING TRAILS:** _____

**ATTRACTIONS:** _____

**RANGER STATION:** _____

**OTHER:** _____

# IMAGES & JOURNAL NOTES

# CAMPSITE LOG

DATE(S): _____

**CAMP:** _____

**LOCATION:** _____

**DIRECTIONS:** _____

**STATE:** _____ **ALTITUDE:** _____ **GPS:** _____

**ROAD CONDITIONS:** _____

**CELL SIGNAL:** _____ **WIFI:** _____ **WEBSITE:** _____

**WEATHER:** _____ **NOISE:** _____ **MAXIMUM STAY:** _____

**PROS:** _____

**CONS:** _____

**TIPS FOR NEXT STAY:** _____

**NOTES:** _____

☆ ☆ ☆ ☆ ☆

## ON-SITE CAMP AMENITIES:

- ☐ Picnic Tables
- ☐ Hiking Trails
- ☐ Boat Dock
- ☐ Pit Toilet

- ☐ Fire Pit
- ☐ Water
- ☐ Shade
- ☐ Views

- ☐ Nature Reserve
- ☐ Historic Sites
- ☐ Fishing
- ☐ OHV Trails
- ☐ Other _____

## NEARBY AMENITIES & NECESSITIES:

**GAS:** _____ **PROPANE:** _____

**GROCERIES:** _____ **C-STORE:** _____

**DRINKING WATER:** _____ **NON-POTABLE WATER:** _____

**DUMP STATION:** _____ **DUMPSTER:** _____

**LAUNDRY:** _____ **SHOWERS:** _____

**FIREWOOD:** _____ **DOG PARK:** _____

**HIKING TRAILS:** _____

**ATTRACTIONS:** _____

**RANGER STATION:** _____

**OTHER:** _____

# IMAGES & JOURNAL NOTES

# CAMPSITE LOG

DATE(S): _____

CAMP: _____

LOCATION: _____

DIRECTIONS: _____

STATE: _____ ALTITUDE: _____ GPS: _____

ROAD CONDITIONS: _____

CELL SIGNAL: _____ WIFI: _____ WEBSITE: _____

WEATHER: _____ NOISE: _____ MAXIMUM STAY: _____

PROS: _____

CONS: _____

TIPS FOR NEXT STAY: _____

NOTES: _____

_____

☆ ☆ ☆ ☆ ☆

## ON-SITE CAMP AMENITIES:

- ☐ Picnic Tables
- ☐ Hiking Trails
- ☐ Boat Dock
- ☐ Pit Toilet

- ☐ Fire Pit
- ☐ Water
- ☐ Shade
- ☐ Views

- ☐ Nature Reserve
- ☐ Historic Sites
- ☐ Fishing
- ☐ OHV Trails
- ☐ Other _____

## NEARBY AMENITIES & NECESSITIES:

GAS: _____ PROPANE: _____

GROCERIES: _____ C-STORE: _____

DRINKING WATER: _____ NON-POTABLE WATER: _____

DUMP STATION: _____ DUMPSTER: _____

LAUNDRY: _____ SHOWERS: _____

FIREWOOD: _____ DOG PARK: _____

HIKING TRAILS: _____

ATTRACTIONS: _____

RANGER STATION: _____

OTHER: _____

_____

# IMAGES & JOURNAL NOTES

# CAMPSITE LOG

DATE(S): _____

**CAMP:** _____

**LOCATION:** _____

**DIRECTIONS:** _____

**STATE:** _____ **ALTITUDE:** _____ **GPS:** _____

**ROAD CONDITIONS:** _____

**CELL SIGNAL:** _____ **WIFI:** _____ **WEBSITE:** _____

**WEATHER:** _____ **NOISE:** _____ **MAXIMUM STAY:** _____

**PROS:** _____

**CONS:** _____

**TIPS FOR NEXT STAY:** _____

**NOTES:** _____

☆ ☆ ☆ ☆ ☆

## ON-SITE CAMP AMENITIES:

- ☐ Picnic Tables
- ☐ Hiking Trails
- ☐ Boat Dock
- ☐ Pit Toilet

- ☐ Fire Pit
- ☐ Water
- ☐ Shade
- ☐ Views

- ☐ Nature Reserve
- ☐ Historic Sites
- ☐ Fishing
- ☐ OHV Trails
- ☐ Other _____

## NEARBY AMENITIES & NECESSITIES:

**GAS:** _____ **PROPANE:** _____

**GROCERIES:** _____ **C-STORE:** _____

**DRINKING WATER:** _____ **NON-POTABLE WATER:** _____

**DUMP STATION:** _____ **DUMPSTER:** _____

**LAUNDRY:** _____ **SHOWERS:** _____

**FIREWOOD:** _____ **DOG PARK:** _____

**HIKING TRAILS:** _____

**ATTRACTIONS:** _____

**RANGER STATION:** _____

**OTHER:** _____

# IMAGES & JOURNAL NOTES

# CAMPSITE LOG

DATE(S): _____

**CAMP:** _____

**LOCATION:** _____

**DIRECTIONS:** _____

**STATE:** _____ **ALTITUDE:** _____ **GPS:** _____

**ROAD CONDITIONS:** _____

**CELL SIGNAL:** _____ **WIFI:** _____ **WEBSITE:** _____

**WEATHER:** _____ **NOISE:** _____ **MAXIMUM STAY:** _____

**PROS:** _____

**CONS:** _____

**TIPS FOR NEXT STAY:** _____

**NOTES:** _____

☆ ☆ ☆ ☆ ☆

## ON-SITE CAMP AMENITIES:

- ☐ Picnic Tables
- ☐ Hiking Trails
- ☐ Boat Dock
- ☐ Pit Toilet

- ☐ Fire Pit
- ☐ Water
- ☐ Shade
- ☐ Views

- ☐ Nature Reserve
- ☐ Historic Sites
- ☐ Fishing
- ☐ OHV Trails
- ☐ Other _____

## NEARBY AMENITIES & NECESSITIES:

**GAS:** _____  **PROPANE:** _____

**GROCERIES:** _____  **C-STORE:** _____

**DRINKING WATER:** _____  **NON-POTABLE WATER:** _____

**DUMP STATION:** _____  **DUMPSTER:** _____

**LAUNDRY:** _____  **SHOWERS:** _____

**FIREWOOD:** _____  **DOG PARK:** _____

**HIKING TRAILS:** _____

**ATTRACTIONS:** _____

**RANGER STATION:** _____

**OTHER:** _____

# IMAGES & JOURNAL NOTES

# CAMPSITE LOG

DATE(S): _____

CAMP: _____

LOCATION: _____

DIRECTIONS: _____

STATE: _____ ALTITUDE: _____ GPS: _____

ROAD CONDITIONS: _____

CELL SIGNAL: _____ WIFI: _____ WEBSITE: _____

WEATHER: _____ NOISE: _____ MAXIMUM STAY: _____

PROS: _____

CONS: _____

TIPS FOR NEXT STAY: _____

NOTES: _____

☆ ☆ ☆ ☆ ☆

## ON-SITE CAMP AMENITIES:

☐ Picnic Tables          ☐ Fire Pit          ☐ Nature Reserve
☐ Hiking Trails          ☐ Water             ☐ Historic Sites
☐ Boat Dock              ☐ Shade             ☐ Fishing
☐ Pit Toilet             ☐ Views             ☐ OHV Trails
                                             ☐ Other _____

## NEARBY AMENITIES & NECESSITIES:

GAS: _____          PROPANE: _____

GROCERIES: _____    C-STORE: _____

DRINKING WATER: _____   NON-POTABLE WATER: _____

DUMP STATION: _____   DUMPSTER: _____

LAUNDRY: _____      SHOWERS: _____

FIREWOOD: _____     DOG PARK: _____

HIKING TRAILS: _____

ATTRACTIONS: _____

RANGER STATION: _____

OTHER: _____

# IMAGES & JOURNAL NOTES

# CAMPSITE LOG

DATE(S): _____

CAMP: _____

LOCATION: _____

DIRECTIONS: _____

STATE: _____ ALTITUDE: _____ GPS: _____

ROAD CONDITIONS: _____

CELL SIGNAL: _____ WIFI: _____ WEBSITE: _____

WEATHER: _____ NOISE: _____ MAXIMUM STAY: _____

PROS: _____

CONS: _____

TIPS FOR NEXT STAY: _____

NOTES: _____

☆ ☆ ☆ ☆ ☆

## ON-SITE CAMP AMENITIES:

- ☐ Picnic Tables
- ☐ Hiking Trails
- ☐ Boat Dock
- ☐ Pit Toilet

- ☐ Fire Pit
- ☐ Water
- ☐ Shade
- ☐ Views

- ☐ Nature Reserve
- ☐ Historic Sites
- ☐ Fishing
- ☐ OHV Trails
- ☐ Other _____

## NEARBY AMENITIES & NECESSITIES:

GAS: _____ PROPANE: _____

GROCERIES: _____ C-STORE: _____

DRINKING WATER: _____ NON-POTABLE WATER: _____

DUMP STATION: _____ DUMPSTER: _____

LAUNDRY: _____ SHOWERS: _____

FIREWOOD: _____ DOG PARK: _____

HIKING TRAILS: _____

ATTRACTIONS: _____

RANGER STATION: _____

OTHER: _____

# IMAGES & JOURNAL NOTES

# CAMPSITE LOG

DATE(S): _____

**CAMP:** _____

**LOCATION:** _____

**DIRECTIONS:** _____

**STATE:** _____ **ALTITUDE:** _____ **GPS:** _____

**ROAD CONDITIONS:** _____

**CELL SIGNAL:** _____ **WIFI:** _____ **WEBSITE:** _____

**WEATHER:** _____ **NOISE:** _____ **MAXIMUM STAY:** _____

**PROS:** _____

**CONS:** _____

**TIPS FOR NEXT STAY:** _____

**NOTES:** _____

☆ ☆ ☆ ☆ ☆

## ON-SITE CAMP AMENITIES:

☐ Picnic Tables  ☐ Fire Pit  ☐ Nature Reserve
☐ Hiking Trails  ☐ Water  ☐ Historic Sites
☐ Boat Dock  ☐ Shade  ☐ Fishing
☐ Pit Toilet  ☐ Views  ☐ OHV Trails
☐ Other _____

## NEARBY AMENITIES & NECESSITIES:

**GAS:** _____ **PROPANE:** _____

**GROCERIES:** _____ **C-STORE:** _____

**DRINKING WATER:** _____ **NON-POTABLE WATER:** _____

**DUMP STATION:** _____ **DUMPSTER:** _____

**LAUNDRY:** _____ **SHOWERS:** _____

**FIREWOOD:** _____ **DOG PARK:** _____

**HIKING TRAILS:** _____

**ATTRACTIONS:** _____

**RANGER STATION:** _____

**OTHER:** _____

# IMAGES & JOURNAL NOTES

# CAMPSITE LOG

DATE(S): _____

**CAMP:** _____

**LOCATION:** _____

**DIRECTIONS:** _____

**STATE:** _____ **ALTITUDE:** _____ **GPS:** _____

**ROAD CONDITIONS:** _____

**CELL SIGNAL:** _____ **WIFI:** _____ **WEBSITE:** _____

**WEATHER:** _____ **NOISE:** _____ **MAXIMUM STAY:** _____

**PROS:** _____

**CONS:** _____

**TIPS FOR NEXT STAY:** _____

**NOTES:** _____

☆ ☆ ☆ ☆ ☆

## ON-SITE CAMP AMENITIES:

- ☐ Picnic Tables
- ☐ Hiking Trails
- ☐ Boat Dock
- ☐ Pit Toilet

- ☐ Fire Pit
- ☐ Water
- ☐ Shade
- ☐ Views

- ☐ Nature Reserve
- ☐ Historic Sites
- ☐ Fishing
- ☐ OHV Trails
- ☐ Other _____

## NEARBY AMENITIES & NECESSITIES:

**GAS:** _____ **PROPANE:** _____

**GROCERIES:** _____ **C-STORE:** _____

**DRINKING WATER:** _____ **NON-POTABLE WATER:** _____

**DUMP STATION:** _____ **DUMPSTER:** _____

**LAUNDRY:** _____ **SHOWERS:** _____

**FIREWOOD:** _____ **DOG PARK:** _____

**HIKING TRAILS:** _____

**ATTRACTIONS:** _____

**RANGER STATION:** _____

**OTHER:** _____

# IMAGES & JOURNAL NOTES

# CAMPSITE LOG

DATE(S): _____

CAMP: _____

LOCATION: _____

DIRECTIONS: _____

STATE: _____ ALTITUDE: _____ GPS: _____

ROAD CONDITIONS: _____

CELL SIGNAL: _____ WIFI: _____ WEBSITE: _____

WEATHER: _____ NOISE: _____ MAXIMUM STAY: _____

PROS: _____

CONS: _____

TIPS FOR NEXT STAY: _____

NOTES: _____

☆ ☆ ☆ ☆ ☆

## ON-SITE CAMP AMENITIES:

☐ Picnic Tables      ☐ Fire Pit      ☐ Nature Reserve
☐ Hiking Trails      ☐ Water         ☐ Historic Sites
☐ Boat Dock          ☐ Shade         ☐ Fishing
☐ Pit Toilet         ☐ Views         ☐ OHV Trails
                                     ☐ Other _____

## NEARBY AMENITIES & NECESSITIES:

GAS: _____                PROPANE: _____

GROCERIES: _____          C-STORE: _____

DRINKING WATER: _____     NON-POTABLE WATER: _____

DUMP STATION: _____       DUMPSTER: _____

LAUNDRY: _____            SHOWERS: _____

FIREWOOD: _____           DOG PARK: _____

HIKING TRAILS: _____

ATTRACTIONS: _____

RANGER STATION: _____

OTHER: _____

# IMAGES & JOURNAL NOTES

# CAMPSITE LOG

DATE(S): _____

**CAMP:** _____

**LOCATION:** _____

**DIRECTIONS:** _____

**STATE:** _____ **ALTITUDE:** _____ **GPS:** _____

**ROAD CONDITIONS:** _____

**CELL SIGNAL:** _____ **WIFI:** _____ **WEBSITE:** _____

**WEATHER:** _____ **NOISE:** _____ **MAXIMUM STAY:** _____

**PROS:** _____

**CONS:** _____

**TIPS FOR NEXT STAY:** _____

**NOTES:** _____

☆ ☆ ☆ ☆ ☆

## ON-SITE CAMP AMENITIES:

- ☐ Picnic Tables
- ☐ Hiking Trails
- ☐ Boat Dock
- ☐ Pit Toilet

- ☐ Fire Pit
- ☐ Water
- ☐ Shade
- ☐ Views

- ☐ Nature Reserve
- ☐ Historic Sites
- ☐ Fishing
- ☐ OHV Trails
- ☐ Other _____

## NEARBY AMENITIES & NECESSITIES:

**GAS:** _____ **PROPANE:** _____

**GROCERIES:** _____ **C-STORE:** _____

**DRINKING WATER:** _____ **NON-POTABLE WATER:** _____

**DUMP STATION:** _____ **DUMPSTER:** _____

**LAUNDRY:** _____ **SHOWERS:** _____

**FIREWOOD:** _____ **DOG PARK:** _____

**HIKING TRAILS:** _____

**ATTRACTIONS:** _____

**RANGER STATION:** _____

**OTHER:** _____

# IMAGES & JOURNAL NOTES

# CAMPSITE LOG

DATE(S): _____

**CAMP:** _____

**LOCATION:** _____

**DIRECTIONS:** _____

**STATE:** _____ **ALTITUDE:** _____ **GPS:** _____

**ROAD CONDITIONS:** _____

**CELL SIGNAL:** _____ **WIFI:** _____ **WEBSITE:** _____

**WEATHER:** _____ **NOISE:** _____ **MAXIMUM STAY:** _____

**PROS:** _____

**CONS:** _____

**TIPS FOR NEXT STAY:** _____

**NOTES:** _____

☆ ☆ ☆ ☆ ☆

## ON-SITE CAMP AMENITIES:

- ☐ Picnic Tables
- ☐ Hiking Trails
- ☐ Boat Dock
- ☐ Pit Toilet

- ☐ Fire Pit
- ☐ Water
- ☐ Shade
- ☐ Views

- ☐ Nature Reserve
- ☐ Historic Sites
- ☐ Fishing
- ☐ OHV Trails
- ☐ Other _____

## NEARBY AMENITIES & NECESSITIES:

**GAS:** _____ **PROPANE:** _____

**GROCERIES:** _____ **C-STORE:** _____

**DRINKING WATER:** _____ **NON-POTABLE WATER:** _____

**DUMP STATION:** _____ **DUMPSTER:** _____

**LAUNDRY:** _____ **SHOWERS:** _____

**FIREWOOD:** _____ **DOG PARK:** _____

**HIKING TRAILS:** _____

**ATTRACTIONS:** _____

**RANGER STATION:** _____

**OTHER:** _____

# IMAGES & JOURNAL NOTES

# CAMPSITE LOG

DATE(S): _____

**CAMP:** _____

**LOCATION:** _____

**DIRECTIONS:** _____

**STATE:** _____ **ALTITUDE:** _____ **GPS:** _____

**ROAD CONDITIONS:** _____

**CELL SIGNAL:** _____ **WIFI:** _____ **WEBSITE:** _____

**WEATHER:** _____ **NOISE:** _____ **MAXIMUM STAY:** _____

**PROS:** _____

**CONS:** _____

**TIPS FOR NEXT STAY:** _____

**NOTES:** _____

☆ ☆ ☆ ☆ ☆

## ON-SITE CAMP AMENITIES:

- ☐ Picnic Tables
- ☐ Hiking Trails
- ☐ Boat Dock
- ☐ Pit Toilet

- ☐ Fire Pit
- ☐ Water
- ☐ Shade
- ☐ Views

- ☐ Nature Reserve
- ☐ Historic Sites
- ☐ Fishing
- ☐ OHV Trails
- ☐ Other _____

## NEARBY AMENITIES & NECESSITIES:

**GAS:** _____ **PROPANE:** _____

**GROCERIES:** _____ **C-STORE:** _____

**DRINKING WATER:** _____ **NON-POTABLE WATER:** _____

**DUMP STATION:** _____ **DUMPSTER:** _____

**LAUNDRY:** _____ **SHOWERS:** _____

**FIREWOOD:** _____ **DOG PARK:** _____

**HIKING TRAILS:** _____

**ATTRACTIONS:** _____

**RANGER STATION:** _____

**OTHER:** _____

# IMAGES & JOURNAL NOTES

# CAMPSITE LOG

DATE(S): _____

**CAMP:** _____

**LOCATION:** _____

**DIRECTIONS:** _____

**STATE:** _____ **ALTITUDE:** _____ **GPS:** _____

**ROAD CONDITIONS:** _____

**CELL SIGNAL:** _____ **WIFI:** _____ **WEBSITE:** _____

**WEATHER:** _____ **NOISE:** _____ **MAXIMUM STAY:** _____

**PROS:** _____

**CONS:** _____

**TIPS FOR NEXT STAY:** _____

**NOTES:** _____

☆ ☆ ☆ ☆ ☆

## ON-SITE CAMP AMENITIES:

- ☐ Picnic Tables
- ☐ Hiking Trails
- ☐ Boat Dock
- ☐ Pit Toilet

- ☐ Fire Pit
- ☐ Water
- ☐ Shade
- ☐ Views

- ☐ Nature Reserve
- ☐ Historic Sites
- ☐ Fishing
- ☐ OHV Trails
- ☐ Other _____

## NEARBY AMENITIES & NECESSITIES:

**GAS:** _____ **PROPANE:** _____

**GROCERIES:** _____ **C-STORE:** _____

**DRINKING WATER:** _____ **NON-POTABLE WATER:** _____

**DUMP STATION:** _____ **DUMPSTER:** _____

**LAUNDRY:** _____ **SHOWERS:** _____

**FIREWOOD:** _____ **DOG PARK:** _____

**HIKING TRAILS:** _____

**ATTRACTIONS:** _____

**RANGER STATION:** _____

**OTHER:** _____

# IMAGES & JOURNAL NOTES

_____
_____
_____
_____
_____
_____
_____
_____
_____
_____
_____
_____
_____
_____
_____
_____

# CAMPSITE LOG

DATE(S): _____

**CAMP:** _____

**LOCATION:** _____

**DIRECTIONS:** _____

**STATE:** _____ **ALTITUDE:** _____ **GPS:** _____

**ROAD CONDITIONS:** _____

**CELL SIGNAL:** _____ **WIFI:** _____ **WEBSITE:** _____

**WEATHER:** _____ **NOISE:** _____ **MAXIMUM STAY:** _____

**PROS:** _____

**CONS:** _____

**TIPS FOR NEXT STAY:** _____

**NOTES:** _____

☆ ☆ ☆ ☆ ☆

## ON-SITE CAMP AMENITIES:

☐ Nature Reserve

☐ Picnic Tables     ☐ Fire Pit     ☐ Historic Sites

☐ Hiking Trails     ☐ Water     ☐ Fishing

☐ Boat Dock     ☐ Shade     ☐ OHV Trails

☐ Pit Toilet     ☐ Views     ☐ Other _____

## NEARBY AMENITIES & NECESSITIES:

**GAS:** _____ **PROPANE:** _____

**GROCERIES:** _____ **C-STORE:** _____

**DRINKING WATER:** _____ **NON-POTABLE WATER:** _____

**DUMP STATION:** _____ **DUMPSTER:** _____

**LAUNDRY:** _____ **SHOWERS:** _____

**FIREWOOD:** _____ **DOG PARK:** _____

**HIKING TRAILS:** _____

**ATTRACTIONS:** _____

**RANGER STATION:** _____

**OTHER:** _____

# IMAGES & JOURNAL NOTES

# CAMPSITE LOG

DATE(S): _____

**CAMP:** _____

**LOCATION:** _____

**DIRECTIONS:** _____

**STATE:** _____ **ALTITUDE:** _____ **GPS:** _____

**ROAD CONDITIONS:** _____

**CELL SIGNAL:** _____ **WIFI:** _____ **WEBSITE:** _____

**WEATHER:** _____ **NOISE:** _____ **MAXIMUM STAY:** _____

**PROS:** _____

**CONS:** _____

**TIPS FOR NEXT STAY:** _____

**NOTES:** _____

☆ ☆ ☆ ☆ ☆

## ON-SITE CAMP AMENITIES:

☐ Picnic Tables　　☐ Fire Pit　　☐ Nature Reserve
☐ Hiking Trails　　☐ Water　　☐ Historic Sites
☐ Boat Dock　　☐ Shade　　☐ Fishing
☐ Pit Toilet　　☐ Views　　☐ OHV Trails
　　　　　　　　　　　　　　☐ Other _____

## NEARBY AMENITIES & NECESSITIES:

**GAS:** _____ **PROPANE:** _____

**GROCERIES:** _____ **C-STORE:** _____

**DRINKING WATER:** _____ **NON-POTABLE WATER:** _____

**DUMP STATION:** _____ **DUMPSTER:** _____

**LAUNDRY:** _____ **SHOWERS:** _____

**FIREWOOD:** _____ **DOG PARK:** _____

**HIKING TRAILS:** _____

**ATTRACTIONS:** _____

**RANGER STATION:** _____

**OTHER:** _____

# IMAGES & JOURNAL NOTES

# CAMPSITE LOG

DATE(S): _____

**CAMP:** _____

**LOCATION:** _____

DIRECTIONS: _____

STATE: _____ ALTITUDE: _____ GPS: _____

ROAD CONDITIONS: _____

CELL SIGNAL: _____ WIFI: _____ WEBSITE: _____

WEATHER: _____ NOISE: _____ MAXIMUM STAY: _____

PROS: _____

CONS: _____

TIPS FOR NEXT STAY: _____

NOTES: _____

☆ ☆ ☆ ☆ ☆

## ON-SITE CAMP AMENITIES:

- ☐ Picnic Tables
- ☐ Hiking Trails
- ☐ Boat Dock
- ☐ Pit Toilet

- ☐ Fire Pit
- ☐ Water
- ☐ Shade
- ☐ Views

- ☐ Nature Reserve
- ☐ Historic Sites
- ☐ Fishing
- ☐ OHV Trails
- ☐ Other _____

## NEARBY AMENITIES & NECESSITIES:

GAS: _____ PROPANE: _____

GROCERIES: _____ C-STORE: _____

DRINKING WATER: _____ NON-POTABLE WATER: _____

DUMP STATION: _____ DUMPSTER: _____

LAUNDRY: _____ SHOWERS: _____

FIREWOOD: _____ DOG PARK: _____

HIKING TRAILS: _____

ATTRACTIONS: _____

RANGER STATION: _____

OTHER: _____

# IMAGES & JOURNAL NOTES

# CAMPSITE LOG

DATE(S): _____

**CAMP:** _____

**LOCATION:** _____

**DIRECTIONS:** _____

**STATE:** _____ **ALTITUDE:** _____ **GPS:** _____

**ROAD CONDITIONS:** _____

**CELL SIGNAL:** _____ **WIFI:** _____ **WEBSITE:** _____

**WEATHER:** _____ **NOISE:** _____ **MAXIMUM STAY:** _____

**PROS:** _____

**CONS:** _____

**TIPS FOR NEXT STAY:** _____

**NOTES:** _____

☆ ☆ ☆ ☆ ☆

## ON-SITE CAMP AMENITIES:

- ☐ Picnic Tables
- ☐ Hiking Trails
- ☐ Boat Dock
- ☐ Pit Toilet

- ☐ Fire Pit
- ☐ Water
- ☐ Shade
- ☐ Views

- ☐ Nature Reserve
- ☐ Historic Sites
- ☐ Fishing
- ☐ OHV Trails
- ☐ Other _____

## NEARBY AMENITIES & NECESSITIES:

**GAS:** _____ **PROPANE:** _____

**GROCERIES:** _____ **C-STORE:** _____

**DRINKING WATER:** _____ **NON-POTABLE WATER:** _____

**DUMP STATION:** _____ **DUMPSTER:** _____

**LAUNDRY:** _____ **SHOWERS:** _____

**FIREWOOD:** _____ **DOG PARK:** _____

**HIKING TRAILS:** _____

**ATTRACTIONS:** _____

**RANGER STATION:** _____

**OTHER:** _____

# IMAGES & JOURNAL NOTES

# CAMPSITE LOG

DATE(S): _____

**CAMP:** _____

**LOCATION:** _____

**DIRECTIONS:** _____

**STATE:** _____ **ALTITUDE:** _____ **GPS:** _____

**ROAD CONDITIONS:** _____

**CELL SIGNAL:** _____ **WIFI:** _____ **WEBSITE:** _____

**WEATHER:** _____ **NOISE:** _____ **MAXIMUM STAY:** _____

**PROS:** _____

**CONS:** _____

**TIPS FOR NEXT STAY:** _____

**NOTES:** _____

☆ ☆ ☆ ☆ ☆

## ON-SITE CAMP AMENITIES:

- ☐ Picnic Tables
- ☐ Hiking Trails
- ☐ Boat Dock
- ☐ Pit Toilet

- ☐ Fire Pit
- ☐ Water
- ☐ Shade
- ☐ Views

- ☐ Nature Reserve
- ☐ Historic Sites
- ☐ Fishing
- ☐ OHV Trails
- ☐ Other _____

## NEARBY AMENITIES & NECESSITIES:

**GAS:** _____  **PROPANE:** _____

**GROCERIES:** _____  **C-STORE:** _____

**DRINKING WATER:** _____  **NON-POTABLE WATER:** _____

**DUMP STATION:** _____  **DUMPSTER:** _____

**LAUNDRY:** _____  **SHOWERS:** _____

**FIREWOOD:** _____  **DOG PARK:** _____

**HIKING TRAILS:** _____

**ATTRACTIONS:** _____

**RANGER STATION:** _____

**OTHER:** _____

# IMAGES & JOURNAL NOTES

# CAMPSITE LOG

DATE(S): _____

**CAMP:** _____

**LOCATION:** _____

**DIRECTIONS:** _____

**STATE:** _____ **ALTITUDE:** _____ **GPS:** _____

**ROAD CONDITIONS:** _____

**CELL SIGNAL:** _____ **WIFI:** _____ **WEBSITE:** _____

**WEATHER:** _____ **NOISE:** _____ **MAXIMUM STAY:** _____

**PROS:** _____

**CONS:** _____

**TIPS FOR NEXT STAY:** _____

**NOTES:** _____

☆ ☆ ☆ ☆ ☆

## ON-SITE CAMP AMENITIES:

- ☐ Picnic Tables
- ☐ Hiking Trails
- ☐ Boat Dock
- ☐ Pit Toilet

- ☐ Fire Pit
- ☐ Water
- ☐ Shade
- ☐ Views

- ☐ Nature Reserve
- ☐ Historic Sites
- ☐ Fishing
- ☐ OHV Trails
- ☐ Other _____

## NEARBY AMENITIES & NECESSITIES:

**GAS:** _____ **PROPANE:** _____

**GROCERIES:** _____ **C-STORE:** _____

**DRINKING WATER:** _____ **NON-POTABLE WATER:** _____

**DUMP STATION:** _____ **DUMPSTER:** _____

**LAUNDRY:** _____ **SHOWERS:** _____

**FIREWOOD:** _____ **DOG PARK:** _____

**HIKING TRAILS:** _____

**ATTRACTIONS:** _____

**RANGER STATION:** _____

**OTHER:** _____

# IMAGES & JOURNAL NOTES

# CAMPSITE LOG

DATE(S): _____

CAMP: _____

LOCATION: _____

DIRECTIONS: _____

STATE: _____ ALTITUDE: _____ GPS: _____

ROAD CONDITIONS: _____

CELL SIGNAL: _____ WIFI: _____ WEBSITE: _____

WEATHER: _____ NOISE: _____ MAXIMUM STAY: _____

PROS: _____

CONS: _____

TIPS FOR NEXT STAY: _____

NOTES: _____

☆ ☆ ☆ ☆ ☆

## ON-SITE CAMP AMENITIES:

☐ Picnic Tables        ☐ Fire Pit        ☐ Nature Reserve
☐ Hiking Trails        ☐ Water           ☐ Historic Sites
☐ Boat Dock            ☐ Shade           ☐ Fishing
☐ Pit Toilet           ☐ Views           ☐ OHV Trails
                                          ☐ Other _____

## NEARBY AMENITIES & NECESSITIES:

GAS: _____                    PROPANE: _____

GROCERIES: _____              C-STORE: _____

DRINKING WATER: _____         NON-POTABLE WATER: _____

DUMP STATION: _____           DUMPSTER: _____

LAUNDRY: _____                SHOWERS: _____

FIREWOOD: _____               DOG PARK: _____

HIKING TRAILS: _____

ATTRACTIONS: _____

RANGER STATION: _____

OTHER: _____

# IMAGES & JOURNAL NOTES

# Mileage Log

# MILEAGE LOG

| Date | From/Destination | Odometer | | Total Miles | Note |
|---|---|---|---|---|---|
| | | Start | End | | |
| | | | | | |
| | | | | | |
| | | | | | |
| | | | | | |
| | | | | | |
| | | | | | |
| | | | | | |
| | | | | | |
| | | | | | |
| | | | | | |
| | | | | | |
| | | | | | |
| | | | | | |
| | | | | | |
| | | | | | |
| | | | | | |
| | | | | | |
| | | | | | |
| | | | | | |
| | | | | | |
| | | | | | |
| | | | | | |

# MILEAGE LOG

| Date | From/Destination | Odometer | | Total Miles | Note |
|------|------------------|----------|-----|-------------|------|
| | | Start | End | | |
| | | | | | |
| | | | | | |
| | | | | | |
| | | | | | |
| | | | | | |
| | | | | | |
| | | | | | |
| | | | | | |
| | | | | | |
| | | | | | |
| | | | | | |
| | | | | | |
| | | | | | |
| | | | | | |
| | | | | | |
| | | | | | |
| | | | | | |
| | | | | | |
| | | | | | |
| | | | | | |
| | | | | | |
| | | | | | |

# MILEAGE LOG

| Date | From/Destination | Odometer | | Total Miles | Note |
|------|------------------|----------|-----|-------------|------|
| | | Start | End | | |
| | | | | | |
| | | | | | |
| | | | | | |
| | | | | | |
| | | | | | |
| | | | | | |
| | | | | | |
| | | | | | |
| | | | | | |
| | | | | | |
| | | | | | |
| | | | | | |
| | | | | | |
| | | | | | |
| | | | | | |
| | | | | | |
| | | | | | |
| | | | | | |
| | | | | | |
| | | | | | |
| | | | | | |
| | | | | | |

# MILEAGE LOG

| Date | From/Destination | Odometer Start | Odometer End | Total Miles | Note |
|---|---|---|---|---|---|
| | | | | | |
| | | | | | |
| | | | | | |
| | | | | | |
| | | | | | |
| | | | | | |
| | | | | | |
| | | | | | |
| | | | | | |
| | | | | | |
| | | | | | |
| | | | | | |
| | | | | | |
| | | | | | |
| | | | | | |
| | | | | | |
| | | | | | |
| | | | | | |
| | | | | | |
| | | | | | |
| | | | | | |
| | | | | | |

# MILEAGE LOG

| Date | From/Destination | Odometer | | Total Miles | Note |
|---|---|---|---|---|---|
| | | Start | End | | |
| | | | | | |
| | | | | | |
| | | | | | |
| | | | | | |
| | | | | | |
| | | | | | |
| | | | | | |
| | | | | | |
| | | | | | |
| | | | | | |
| | | | | | |
| | | | | | |
| | | | | | |
| | | | | | |
| | | | | | |
| | | | | | |
| | | | | | |
| | | | | | |
| | | | | | |
| | | | | | |

# MILEAGE LOG

| Date | From/Destination | Odometer | | Total Miles | Note |
|------|------------------|----------|------|-------------|------|
| | | Start | End | | |
| | | | | | |
| | | | | | |
| | | | | | |
| | | | | | |
| | | | | | |
| | | | | | |
| | | | | | |
| | | | | | |
| | | | | | |
| | | | | | |
| | | | | | |
| | | | | | |
| | | | | | |
| | | | | | |
| | | | | | |
| | | | | | |
| | | | | | |
| | | | | | |
| | | | | | |
| | | | | | |
| | | | | | |
| | | | | | |
| | | | | | |

# MILEAGE LOG

| Date | From/Destination | Odometer | | Total Miles | Note |
|------|------------------|----------|-----|-------------|------|
| | | Start | End | | |
| | | | | | |
| | | | | | |
| | | | | | |
| | | | | | |
| | | | | | |
| | | | | | |
| | | | | | |
| | | | | | |
| | | | | | |
| | | | | | |
| | | | | | |
| | | | | | |
| | | | | | |
| | | | | | |
| | | | | | |
| | | | | | |
| | | | | | |
| | | | | | |
| | | | | | |
| | | | | | |
| | | | | | |
| | | | | | |

# MILEAGE LOG

| Date | From/Destination | Odometer | | Total Miles | Note |
|------|------------------|----------|-----|-------------|------|
| | | Start | End | | |
| | | | | | |
| | | | | | |
| | | | | | |
| | | | | | |
| | | | | | |
| | | | | | |
| | | | | | |
| | | | | | |
| | | | | | |
| | | | | | |
| | | | | | |
| | | | | | |
| | | | | | |
| | | | | | |
| | | | | | |
| | | | | | |
| | | | | | |
| | | | | | |
| | | | | | |
| | | | | | |
| | | | | | |
| | | | | | |

# MILEAGE LOG

| Date | From/Destination | Odometer | | Total Miles | Note |
|------|------------------|----------|-----|-------------|------|
|      |                  | Start | End |          |      |
|      |                  |       |     |          |      |
|      |                  |       |     |          |      |
|      |                  |       |     |          |      |
|      |                  |       |     |          |      |
|      |                  |       |     |          |      |
|      |                  |       |     |          |      |
|      |                  |       |     |          |      |
|      |                  |       |     |          |      |
|      |                  |       |     |          |      |
|      |                  |       |     |          |      |
|      |                  |       |     |          |      |
|      |                  |       |     |          |      |
|      |                  |       |     |          |      |
|      |                  |       |     |          |      |
|      |                  |       |     |          |      |
|      |                  |       |     |          |      |
|      |                  |       |     |          |      |
|      |                  |       |     |          |      |
|      |                  |       |     |          |      |
|      |                  |       |     |          |      |
|      |                  |       |     |          |      |

# MILEAGE LOG

| Date | From/Destination | Odometer | | Total Miles | Note |
|------|------------------|----------|-----|-------------|------|
|      |                  | Start | End |             |      |
|      |                  |       |     |             |      |
|      |                  |       |     |             |      |
|      |                  |       |     |             |      |
|      |                  |       |     |             |      |
|      |                  |       |     |             |      |
|      |                  |       |     |             |      |
|      |                  |       |     |             |      |
|      |                  |       |     |             |      |
|      |                  |       |     |             |      |
|      |                  |       |     |             |      |
|      |                  |       |     |             |      |
|      |                  |       |     |             |      |
|      |                  |       |     |             |      |
|      |                  |       |     |             |      |
|      |                  |       |     |             |      |
|      |                  |       |     |             |      |
|      |                  |       |     |             |      |
|      |                  |       |     |             |      |
|      |                  |       |     |             |      |
|      |                  |       |     |             |      |
|      |                  |       |     |             |      |
|      |                  |       |     |             |      |
|      |                  |       |     |             |      |

# MILEAGE LOG

| Date | From/Destination | Odometer | | Total Miles | Note |
|------|------------------|----------|-----|-------------|------|
| | | Start | End | | |
| | | | | | |
| | | | | | |
| | | | | | |
| | | | | | |
| | | | | | |
| | | | | | |
| | | | | | |
| | | | | | |
| | | | | | |
| | | | | | |
| | | | | | |
| | | | | | |
| | | | | | |
| | | | | | |
| | | | | | |
| | | | | | |
| | | | | | |
| | | | | | |
| | | | | | |
| | | | | | |
| | | | | | |
| | | | | | |

# Recommended
# Campsites

# RECOMMENDED CAMPSITES

| STATE | LOCATION |
|---|---|
| | |
| | |
| | |
| | |
| | |
| | |
| | |
| | |
| | |
| | |
| | |
| | |

# RECOMMENDED CAMPSITES

| STATE | LOCATION |
|-------|----------|
|       |          |
|       |          |
|       |          |
|       |          |
|       |          |
|       |          |
|       |          |
|       |          |
|       |          |
|       |          |
|       |          |
|       |          |
|       |          |
|       |          |
|       |          |
|       |          |
|       |          |
|       |          |
|       |          |
|       |          |
|       |          |
|       |          |

# RECOMMENDED CAMPSITES

| STATE | LOCATION |
|-------|----------|
|       |          |
|       |          |
|       |          |
|       |          |
|       |          |
|       |          |
|       |          |
|       |          |
|       |          |
|       |          |
|       |          |
|       |          |
|       |          |
|       |          |
|       |          |
|       |          |
|       |          |
|       |          |
|       |          |
|       |          |

# RECOMMENDED CAMPSITES

| STATE | LOCATION |
|-------|----------|
|       |          |
|       |          |
|       |          |
|       |          |
|       |          |
|       |          |
|       |          |
|       |          |
|       |          |
|       |          |
|       |          |
|       |          |
|       |          |
|       |          |
|       |          |
|       |          |
|       |          |
|       |          |
|       |          |
|       |          |
|       |          |
|       |          |

# RECOMMENDED CAMPSITES

| STATE | LOCATION |
|---|---|
| | |
| | |
| | |
| | |
| | |
| | |
| | |
| | |
| | |
| | |
| | |
| | |
| | |
| | |
| | |
| | |
| | |
| | |
| | |
| | |

# People We Meet
# Along the Way

# PEOPLE WE MEET ALONG THE WAY

**Name**

Address

City                State                Zip

Phone

Email

**Name**

Address

City                State                Zip

Phone

Email

**Name**

Address

City                State                Zip

Phone

Email

**Name**

Address

City                State                Zip

Phone

Email

**Name**

Address

City                State                Zip

Phone

Email

**Name**

Address

City                State                Zip

Phone

Email

**Name**

Address

City                State                Zip

Phone

Email

**Name**

Address

City                State                Zip

Phone

Email

# PEOPLE WE MEET ALONG THE WAY

**Name**

Address

City                State        Zip

Phone

Email

**Name**

Address

City                State        Zip

Phone

Email

**Name**

Address

City                State        Zip

Phone

Email

**Name**

Address

City                State        Zip

Phone

Email

**Name**

Address

City                State        Zip

Phone

Email

**Name**

Address

City                State        Zip

Phone

Email

**Name**

Address

City                State        Zip

Phone

Email

**Name**

Address

City                State        Zip

Phone

Email

# PEOPLE WE MEET ALONG THE WAY

**Name**

Address

City                State        Zip

Phone

Email

**Name**

Address

City                State        Zip

Phone

Email

**Name**

Address

City                State        Zip

Phone

Email

**Name**

Address

City                State        Zip

Phone

Email

**Name**

Address

City                State        Zip

Phone

Email

**Name**

Address

City                State        Zip

Phone

Email

**Name**

Address

City                State        Zip

Phone

Email

**Name**

Address

City                State        Zip

Phone

Email

# PEOPLE WE MEET ALONG THE WAY

**Name**

Address

City      State      Zip

Phone

Email

**Name**

Address

City      State      Zip

Phone

Email

**Name**

Address

City      State      Zip

Phone

Email

**Name**

Address

City      State      Zip

Phone

Email

**Name**

Address

City      State      Zip

Phone

Email

**Name**

Address

City      State      Zip

Phone

Email

**Name**

Address

City      State      Zip

Phone

Email

**Name**

Address

City      State      Zip

Phone

Email

# PEOPLE WE MEET ALONG THE WAY

**Name**

Address

City        State       Zip

Phone

Email

**Name**

Address

City        State       Zip

Phone

Email

**Name**

Address

City        State       Zip

Phone

Email

**Name**

Address

City        State       Zip

Phone

Email

**Name**

Address

City        State       Zip

Phone

Email

**Name**

Address

City        State       Zip

Phone

Email

**Name**

Address

City        State       Zip

Phone

Email

**Name**

Address

City        State       Zip

Phone

Email

# PEOPLE WE MEET ALONG THE WAY

**Name**

Address

City                State            Zip

Phone

Email

**Name**

Address

City                State            Zip

Phone

Email

**Name**

Address

City                State            Zip

Phone

Email

**Name**

Address

City                State            Zip

Phone

Email

**Name**

Address

City                State            Zip

Phone

Email

**Name**

Address

City                State            Zip

Phone

Email

**Name**

Address

City                State            Zip

Phone

Email

**Name**

Address

City                State            Zip

Phone

Email

# PEOPLE WE MEET ALONG THE WAY

**Name**

Address

City                State          Zip

Phone

Email

**Name**

Address

City                State          Zip

Phone

Email

**Name**

Address

City                State          Zip

Phone

Email

**Name**

Address

City                State          Zip

Phone

Email

**Name**

Address

City                State          Zip

Phone

Email

**Name**

Address

City                State          Zip

Phone

Email

**Name**

Address

City                State          Zip

Phone

Email

**Name**

Address

City                State          Zip

Phone

Email

# Helpful Extras

# Inspirational Resources
## Websites, Vlogs, Books & Beyond!

| Format | Name | Topic | Source/Website |
|--------|------|-------|----------------|
|  |  |  |  |
|  |  |  |  |
|  |  |  |  |
|  |  |  |  |
|  |  |  |  |
|  |  |  |  |
|  |  |  |  |
|  |  |  |  |
|  |  |  |  |
|  |  |  |  |
|  |  |  |  |
|  |  |  |  |
|  |  |  |  |
|  |  |  |  |
|  |  |  |  |
|  |  |  |  |
|  |  |  |  |
|  |  |  |  |
|  |  |  |  |
|  |  |  |  |
|  |  |  |  |
|  |  |  |  |

# Inspirational Resources
## Websites, Vlogs, Books & Beyond!

| Format | Name | Topic | Source/Website |
|--------|------|-------|----------------|
| | | | |
| | | | |
| | | | |
| | | | |
| | | | |
| | | | |
| | | | |
| | | | |
| | | | |
| | | | |
| | | | |
| | | | |
| | | | |
| | | | |
| | | | |
| | | | |
| | | | |
| | | | |
| | | | |
| | | | |
| | | | |
| | | | |

# Inspirational Resources
## Websites, Vlogs, Books & Beyond!

| Format | Name | Topic | Source/Website |
|---|---|---|---|
| | | | |
| | | | |
| | | | |
| | | | |
| | | | |
| | | | |
| | | | |
| | | | |
| | | | |
| | | | |
| | | | |
| | | | |
| | | | |
| | | | |
| | | | |
| | | | |
| | | | |
| | | | |
| | | | |
| | | | |
| | | | |

# Inspirational Resources
## Websites, Vlogs, Books & Beyond!

| Format | Name | Topic | Source/Website |
|--------|------|-------|----------------|
|        |      |       |                |
|        |      |       |                |
|        |      |       |                |
|        |      |       |                |
|        |      |       |                |
|        |      |       |                |
|        |      |       |                |
|        |      |       |                |
|        |      |       |                |
|        |      |       |                |
|        |      |       |                |
|        |      |       |                |
|        |      |       |                |
|        |      |       |                |
|        |      |       |                |
|        |      |       |                |
|        |      |       |                |
|        |      |       |                |
|        |      |       |                |
|        |      |       |                |
|        |      |       |                |

# CAMPFIRE RECIPES

RECIPE:

| INGREDIENTS | MAKIN' IT |
|---|---|
| | |

RECIPE:

| INGREDIENTS | MAKIN' IT |
|---|---|
| | |

# CAMPFIRE RECIPES

RECIPE:

INGREDIENTS | MAKIN' IT

RECIPE:

INGREDIENTS | MAKIN' IT

# CAMPFIRE RECIPES

RECIPE:

| INGREDIENTS | MAKIN' IT |
|---|---|
| | |

RECIPE:

| INGREDIENTS | MAKIN' IT |
|---|---|
| | |

# CAMPFIRE RECIPES

RECIPE: _____

| INGREDIENTS | MAKIN' IT |
|---|---|
|  |  |
|  |  |
|  |  |
|  |  |
|  |  |
|  |  |
|  |  |
|  |  |

RECIPE: _____

| INGREDIENTS | MAKIN' IT |
|---|---|
|  |  |
|  |  |
|  |  |
|  |  |
|  |  |
|  |  |
|  |  |

# CAMPFIRE RECIPES

RECIPE:

| INGREDIENTS | MAKIN' IT |
|---|---|
| | |

RECIPE:

| INGREDIENTS | MAKIN' IT |
|---|---|
| | |

# CAMPFIRE RECIPES

RECIPE: _____

| INGREDIENTS | MAKIN' IT |
|---|---|
| | |
| | |
| | |
| | |
| | |
| | |
| | |
| | |

RECIPE: _____

| INGREDIENTS | MAKIN' IT |
|---|---|
| | |
| | |
| | |
| | |
| | |
| | |
| | |

# CAMPFIRE RECIPES

RECIPE:

| INGREDIENTS | MAKIN' IT |
| --- | --- |
| | |
| | |
| | |
| | |
| | |
| | |
| | |
| | |

RECIPE:

| INGREDIENTS | MAKIN' IT |
| --- | --- |
| | |
| | |
| | |
| | |
| | |
| | |
| | |
| | |

# CAMPFIRE RECIPES

RECIPE:

| INGREDIENTS | MAKIN' IT |
|---|---|
| | |

RECIPE:

| INGREDIENTS | MAKIN' IT |
|---|---|
| | |

# 2025

## January

| S | M | T | W | T | F | S |
|---|---|---|---|---|---|---|
|  |  |  | 1 | 2 | 3 | 4 |
| 5 | 6 | 7 | 8 | 9 | 10 | 11 |
| 12 | 13 | 14 | 15 | 16 | 17 | 18 |
| 19 | 20 | 21 | 22 | 23 | 24 | 25 |
| 26 | 27 | 28 | 29 | 30 | 31 |  |

## February

| S | M | T | W | T | F | S |
|---|---|---|---|---|---|---|
|  |  |  |  |  |  | 1 |
| 2 | 3 | 4 | 5 | 6 | 7 | 8 |
| 9 | 10 | 11 | 12 | 13 | 14 | 15 |
| 16 | 17 | 18 | 19 | 20 | 21 | 22 |
| 23 | 24 | 25 | 26 | 27 | 28 |  |

## March

| S | M | T | W | T | F | S |
|---|---|---|---|---|---|---|
|  |  |  |  |  |  | 1 |
| 2 | 3 | 4 | 5 | 6 | 7 | 8 |
| 9 | 10 | 11 | 12 | 13 | 14 | 15 |
| 16 | 17 | 18 | 19 | 20 | 21 | 22 |
| 23 | 24 | 25 | 26 | 27 | 28 | 29 |
| 30 | 31 |  |  |  |  |  |

## April

| S | M | T | W | T | F | S |
|---|---|---|---|---|---|---|
|  |  | 1 | 2 | 3 | 4 | 5 |
| 6 | 7 | 8 | 9 | 10 | 11 | 12 |
| 13 | 14 | 15 | 16 | 17 | 18 | 19 |
| 20 | 21 | 22 | 23 | 24 | 25 | 26 |
| 27 | 28 | 29 | 30 |  |  |  |

## May

| S | M | T | W | T | F | S |
|---|---|---|---|---|---|---|
|  |  |  |  | 1 | 2 | 3 |
| 4 | 5 | 6 | 7 | 8 | 9 | 10 |
| 11 | 12 | 13 | 14 | 15 | 16 | 17 |
| 18 | 19 | 20 | 21 | 22 | 23 | 24 |
| 25 | 26 | 27 | 28 | 29 | 30 | 31 |

## June

| S | M | T | W | T | F | S |
|---|---|---|---|---|---|---|
| 1 | 2 | 3 | 4 | 5 | 6 | 7 |
| 8 | 9 | 10 | 11 | 12 | 13 | 14 |
| 15 | 16 | 17 | 18 | 19 | 20 | 21 |
| 22 | 23 | 24 | 25 | 26 | 27 | 28 |
| 29 | 30 |  |  |  |  |  |

## July

| S | M | T | W | T | F | S |
|---|---|---|---|---|---|---|
|  |  | 1 | 2 | 3 | 4 | 5 |
| 6 | 7 | 8 | 9 | 10 | 11 | 12 |
| 13 | 14 | 15 | 16 | 17 | 18 | 19 |
| 20 | 21 | 22 | 23 | 24 | 25 | 26 |
| 27 | 28 | 29 | 30 | 31 |  |  |

## August

| S | M | T | W | T | F | S |
|---|---|---|---|---|---|---|
|  |  |  |  |  | 1 | 2 |
| 3 | 4 | 5 | 6 | 7 | 8 | 9 |
| 10 | 11 | 12 | 13 | 14 | 15 | 16 |
| 17 | 18 | 19 | 20 | 21 | 22 | 23 |
| 24 | 25 | 26 | 27 | 28 | 29 | 30 |
| 31 |  |  |  |  |  |  |

## September

| S | M | T | W | T | F | S |
|---|---|---|---|---|---|---|
|  | 1 | 2 | 3 | 4 | 5 | 6 |
| 7 | 8 | 9 | 10 | 11 | 12 | 13 |
| 14 | 15 | 16 | 17 | 18 | 19 | 20 |
| 21 | 22 | 23 | 24 | 25 | 26 | 27 |
| 28 | 29 | 30 |  |  |  |  |

## October

| S | M | T | W | T | F | S |
|---|---|---|---|---|---|---|
|  |  |  | 1 | 2 | 3 | 4 |
| 5 | 6 | 7 | 8 | 9 | 10 | 11 |
| 12 | 13 | 14 | 15 | 16 | 17 | 18 |
| 19 | 20 | 21 | 22 | 23 | 24 | 25 |
| 26 | 27 | 28 | 29 | 30 | 31 |  |

## November

| S | M | T | W | T | F | S |
|---|---|---|---|---|---|---|
|  |  |  |  |  |  | 1 |
| 2 | 3 | 4 | 5 | 6 | 7 | 8 |
| 9 | 10 | 11 | 12 | 13 | 14 | 15 |
| 16 | 17 | 18 | 19 | 20 | 21 | 22 |
| 23 | 24 | 25 | 26 | 27 | 28 | 29 |
| 30 |  |  |  |  |  |  |

## December

| S | M | T | W | T | F | S |
|---|---|---|---|---|---|---|
|  | 1 | 2 | 3 | 4 | 5 | 6 |
| 7 | 8 | 9 | 10 | 11 | 12 | 13 |
| 14 | 15 | 16 | 17 | 18 | 19 | 20 |
| 21 | 22 | 23 | 24 | 25 | 26 | 27 |
| 28 | 29 | 30 | 31 |  |  |  |

# 2026

## January

| S | M | T | W | T | F | S |
|---|---|---|---|---|---|---|
|  |  |  |  | 1 | 2 | 3 |
| 4 | 5 | 6 | 7 | 8 | 9 | 10 |
| 11 | 12 | 13 | 14 | 15 | 16 | 17 |
| 18 | 19 | 20 | 21 | 22 | 23 | 24 |
| 25 | 26 | 27 | 28 | 29 | 30 | 31 |

## February

| S | M | T | W | T | F | S |
|---|---|---|---|---|---|---|
| 1 | 2 | 3 | 4 | 5 | 6 | 7 |
| 8 | 9 | 10 | 11 | 12 | 13 | 14 |
| 15 | 16 | 17 | 18 | 19 | 20 | 21 |
| 22 | 23 | 24 | 25 | 26 | 27 | 28 |

## March

| S | M | T | W | T | F | S |
|---|---|---|---|---|---|---|
| 1 | 2 | 3 | 4 | 5 | 6 | 7 |
| 8 | 9 | 10 | 11 | 12 | 13 | 14 |
| 15 | 16 | 17 | 18 | 19 | 20 | 21 |
| 22 | 23 | 24 | 25 | 26 | 27 | 28 |
| 29 | 30 | 31 |  |  |  |  |

## April

| S | M | T | W | T | F | S |
|---|---|---|---|---|---|---|
|  |  |  | 1 | 2 | 3 | 4 |
| 5 | 6 | 7 | 8 | 9 | 10 | 11 |
| 12 | 13 | 14 | 15 | 16 | 17 | 18 |
| 19 | 20 | 21 | 22 | 23 | 24 | 25 |
| 26 | 27 | 28 | 29 | 30 |  |  |

## May

| S | M | T | W | T | F | S |
|---|---|---|---|---|---|---|
|  |  |  |  |  | 1 | 2 |
| 3 | 4 | 5 | 6 | 7 | 8 | 9 |
| 10 | 11 | 12 | 13 | 14 | 15 | 16 |
| 17 | 18 | 19 | 20 | 21 | 22 | 23 |
| 24 | 25 | 26 | 27 | 28 | 29 | 30 |
| 31 |  |  |  |  |  |  |

## June

| S | M | T | W | T | F | S |
|---|---|---|---|---|---|---|
|  | 1 | 2 | 3 | 4 | 5 | 6 |
| 7 | 8 | 9 | 10 | 11 | 12 | 13 |
| 14 | 15 | 16 | 17 | 18 | 19 | 20 |
| 21 | 22 | 23 | 24 | 25 | 26 | 27 |
| 28 | 29 | 30 |  |  |  |  |

## July

| S | M | T | W | T | F | S |
|---|---|---|---|---|---|---|
|  |  |  | 1 | 2 | 3 | 4 |
| 5 | 6 | 7 | 8 | 9 | 10 | 11 |
| 12 | 13 | 14 | 15 | 16 | 17 | 18 |
| 19 | 20 | 21 | 22 | 23 | 24 | 25 |
| 26 | 27 | 28 | 29 | 30 | 31 |  |

## August

| S | M | T | W | T | F | S |
|---|---|---|---|---|---|---|
|  |  |  |  |  |  | 1 |
| 2 | 3 | 4 | 5 | 6 | 7 | 8 |
| 9 | 10 | 11 | 12 | 13 | 14 | 15 |
| 16 | 17 | 18 | 19 | 20 | 21 | 22 |
| 23 | 24 | 25 | 26 | 27 | 28 | 29 |
| 30 | 31 |  |  |  |  |  |

## September

| S | M | T | W | T | F | S |
|---|---|---|---|---|---|---|
|  |  | 1 | 2 | 3 | 4 | 5 |
| 6 | 7 | 8 | 9 | 10 | 11 | 12 |
| 13 | 14 | 15 | 16 | 17 | 18 | 19 |
| 20 | 21 | 22 | 23 | 24 | 25 | 26 |
| 27 | 28 | 29 | 30 |  |  |  |

## October

| S | M | T | W | T | F | S |
|---|---|---|---|---|---|---|
|  |  |  |  | 1 | 2 | 3 |
| 4 | 5 | 6 | 7 | 8 | 9 | 10 |
| 11 | 12 | 13 | 14 | 15 | 16 | 17 |
| 18 | 19 | 20 | 21 | 22 | 23 | 24 |
| 25 | 26 | 27 | 28 | 29 | 30 | 31 |

## November

| S | M | T | W | T | F | S |
|---|---|---|---|---|---|---|
| 1 | 2 | 3 | 4 | 5 | 6 | 7 |
| 8 | 9 | 10 | 11 | 12 | 13 | 14 |
| 15 | 16 | 17 | 18 | 19 | 20 | 21 |
| 22 | 23 | 24 | 25 | 26 | 27 | 28 |
| 29 | 30 |  |  |  |  |  |

## December

| S | M | T | W | T | F | S |
|---|---|---|---|---|---|---|
|  |  | 1 | 2 | 3 | 4 | 5 |
| 6 | 7 | 8 | 9 | 10 | 11 | 12 |
| 13 | 14 | 15 | 16 | 17 | 18 | 19 |
| 20 | 21 | 22 | 23 | 24 | 25 | 26 |
| 27 | 28 | 29 | 30 | 31 |  |  |

# 2027

## January

| S | M | T | W | T | F | S |
|---|---|---|---|---|---|---|
| | | | | | 1 | 2 |
| 3 | 4 | 5 | 6 | 7 | 8 | 9 |
| 10 | 11 | 12 | 13 | 14 | 15 | 16 |
| 17 | 18 | 19 | 20 | 21 | 22 | 23 |
| 24 | 25 | 26 | 27 | 28 | 29 | 30 |
| 31 | | | | | | |

## February

| S | M | T | W | T | F | S |
|---|---|---|---|---|---|---|
| | 1 | 2 | 3 | 4 | 5 | 6 |
| 7 | 8 | 9 | 10 | 11 | 12 | 13 |
| 14 | 15 | 16 | 17 | 18 | 19 | 20 |
| 21 | 22 | 23 | 24 | 25 | 26 | 27 |
| 28 | | | | | | |

## March

| S | M | T | W | T | F | S |
|---|---|---|---|---|---|---|
| | 1 | 2 | 3 | 4 | 5 | 6 |
| 7 | 8 | 9 | 10 | 11 | 12 | 13 |
| 14 | 15 | 16 | 17 | 18 | 19 | 20 |
| 21 | 22 | 23 | 24 | 25 | 26 | 27 |
| 28 | 29 | 30 | 31 | | | |

## April

| S | M | T | W | T | F | S |
|---|---|---|---|---|---|---|
| | | | 1 | 2 | 3 | |
| 4 | 5 | 6 | 7 | 8 | 9 | 10 |
| 11 | 12 | 13 | 14 | 15 | 16 | 17 |
| 18 | 19 | 20 | 21 | 22 | 23 | 24 |
| 25 | 26 | 27 | 28 | 29 | 30 | |

## May

| S | M | T | W | T | F | S |
|---|---|---|---|---|---|---|
| | | | | | | 1 |
| 2 | 3 | 4 | 5 | 6 | 7 | 8 |
| 9 | 10 | 11 | 12 | 13 | 14 | 15 |
| 16 | 17 | 18 | 19 | 20 | 21 | 22 |
| 23 | 24 | 25 | 26 | 27 | 28 | 29 |
| 30 | 31 | | | | | |

## June

| S | M | T | W | T | F | S |
|---|---|---|---|---|---|---|
| | | 1 | 2 | 3 | 4 | 5 |
| 6 | 7 | 8 | 9 | 10 | 11 | 12 |
| 13 | 14 | 15 | 16 | 17 | 18 | 19 |
| 20 | 21 | 22 | 23 | 24 | 25 | 26 |
| 27 | 28 | 29 | 30 | | | |

## July

| S | M | T | W | T | F | S |
|---|---|---|---|---|---|---|
| | | | | 1 | 2 | 3 |
| 4 | 5 | 6 | 7 | 8 | 9 | 10 |
| 11 | 12 | 13 | 14 | 15 | 16 | 17 |
| 18 | 19 | 20 | 21 | 22 | 23 | 24 |
| 25 | 26 | 27 | 28 | 29 | 30 | 31 |

## August

| S | M | T | W | T | F | S |
|---|---|---|---|---|---|---|
| 1 | 2 | 3 | 4 | 5 | 6 | 7 |
| 8 | 9 | 10 | 11 | 12 | 13 | 14 |
| 15 | 16 | 17 | 18 | 19 | 20 | 21 |
| 22 | 23 | 24 | 25 | 26 | 27 | 28 |
| 29 | 30 | 31 | | | | |

## September

| S | M | T | W | T | F | S |
|---|---|---|---|---|---|---|
| | | | 1 | 2 | 3 | 4 |
| 5 | 6 | 7 | 8 | 9 | 10 | 11 |
| 12 | 13 | 14 | 15 | 16 | 17 | 18 |
| 19 | 20 | 21 | 22 | 23 | 24 | 25 |
| 26 | 27 | 28 | 29 | 30 | | |

## October

| S | M | T | W | T | F | S |
|---|---|---|---|---|---|---|
| | | | | | 1 | 2 |
| 3 | 4 | 5 | 6 | 7 | 8 | 9 |
| 10 | 11 | 12 | 13 | 14 | 15 | 16 |
| 17 | 18 | 19 | 20 | 21 | 22 | 23 |
| 24 | 25 | 26 | 27 | 28 | 29 | 30 |
| 31 | | | | | | |

## November

| S | M | T | W | T | F | S |
|---|---|---|---|---|---|---|
| | 1 | 2 | 3 | 4 | 5 | 6 |
| 7 | 8 | 9 | 10 | 11 | 12 | 13 |
| 14 | 15 | 16 | 17 | 18 | 19 | 20 |
| 21 | 22 | 23 | 24 | 25 | 26 | 27 |
| 28 | 29 | 30 | | | | |

## December

| S | M | T | W | T | F | S |
|---|---|---|---|---|---|---|
| | | | 1 | 2 | 3 | 4 |
| 5 | 6 | 7 | 8 | 9 | 10 | 11 |
| 12 | 13 | 14 | 15 | 16 | 17 | 18 |
| 19 | 20 | 21 | 22 | 23 | 24 | 25 |
| 26 | 27 | 28 | 29 | 30 | 31 | |

# 2028

## January

| S | M | T | W | T | F | S |
|---|---|---|---|---|---|---|
|   |   |   |   |   |   | 1 |
| 2 | 3 | 4 | 5 | 6 | 7 | 8 |
| 9 | 10 | 11 | 12 | 13 | 14 | 15 |
| 16 | 17 | 18 | 19 | 20 | 21 | 22 |
| 23 | 24 | 25 | 26 | 27 | 28 | 29 |
| 30 | 31 |   |   |   |   |   |

## February

| S | M | T | W | T | F | S |
|---|---|---|---|---|---|---|
|   |   | 1 | 2 | 3 | 4 | 5 |
| 6 | 7 | 8 | 9 | 10 | 11 | 12 |
| 13 | 14 | 15 | 16 | 17 | 18 | 19 |
| 20 | 21 | 22 | 23 | 24 | 25 | 26 |
| 27 | 28 | 29 |   |   |   |   |

## March

| S | M | T | W | T | F | S |
|---|---|---|---|---|---|---|
|   |   |   | 1 | 2 | 3 | 4 |
| 5 | 6 | 7 | 8 | 9 | 10 | 11 |
| 12 | 13 | 14 | 15 | 16 | 17 | 18 |
| 19 | 20 | 21 | 22 | 23 | 24 | 25 |
| 26 | 27 | 28 | 29 | 30 | 31 |   |

## April

| S | M | T | W | T | F | S |
|---|---|---|---|---|---|---|
|   |   |   |   |   |   | 1 |
| 2 | 3 | 4 | 5 | 6 | 7 | 8 |
| 9 | 10 | 11 | 12 | 13 | 14 | 15 |
| 16 | 17 | 18 | 19 | 20 | 21 | 22 |
| 23 | 24 | 25 | 26 | 27 | 28 | 29 |
| 30 |   |   |   |   |   |   |

## May

| S | M | T | W | T | F | S |
|---|---|---|---|---|---|---|
|   | 1 | 2 | 3 | 4 | 5 | 6 |
| 7 | 8 | 9 | 10 | 11 | 12 | 13 |
| 14 | 15 | 16 | 17 | 18 | 19 | 20 |
| 21 | 22 | 23 | 24 | 25 | 26 | 27 |
| 28 | 29 | 30 | 31 |   |   |   |

## June

| S | M | T | W | T | F | S |
|---|---|---|---|---|---|---|
|   |   |   |   | 1 | 2 | 3 |
| 4 | 5 | 6 | 7 | 8 | 9 | 10 |
| 11 | 12 | 13 | 14 | 15 | 16 | 17 |
| 18 | 19 | 20 | 21 | 22 | 23 | 24 |
| 25 | 26 | 27 | 28 | 29 | 30 |   |

## July

| S | M | T | W | T | F | S |
|---|---|---|---|---|---|---|
|   |   |   |   |   |   | 1 |
| 2 | 3 | 4 | 5 | 6 | 7 | 8 |
| 9 | 10 | 11 | 12 | 13 | 14 | 15 |
| 16 | 17 | 18 | 19 | 20 | 21 | 22 |
| 23 | 24 | 25 | 26 | 27 | 28 | 29 |
| 30 | 31 |   |   |   |   |   |

## August

| S | M | T | W | T | F | S |
|---|---|---|---|---|---|---|
|   |   | 1 | 2 | 3 | 4 | 5 |
| 6 | 7 | 8 | 9 | 10 | 11 | 12 |
| 13 | 14 | 15 | 16 | 17 | 18 | 19 |
| 20 | 21 | 22 | 23 | 24 | 25 | 26 |
| 27 | 28 | 29 | 30 | 31 |   |   |

## September

| S | M | T | W | T | F | S |
|---|---|---|---|---|---|---|
|   |   |   |   |   | 1 | 2 |
| 3 | 4 | 5 | 6 | 7 | 8 | 9 |
| 10 | 11 | 12 | 13 | 14 | 15 | 16 |
| 17 | 18 | 19 | 20 | 21 | 22 | 23 |
| 24 | 25 | 26 | 27 | 28 | 29 | 30 |

## October

| S | M | T | W | T | F | S |
|---|---|---|---|---|---|---|
| 1 | 2 | 3 | 4 | 5 | 6 | 7 |
| 8 | 9 | 10 | 11 | 12 | 13 | 14 |
| 15 | 16 | 17 | 18 | 19 | 20 | 21 |
| 22 | 23 | 24 | 25 | 26 | 27 | 28 |
| 29 | 30 | 31 |   |   |   |   |

## November

| S | M | T | W | T | F | S |
|---|---|---|---|---|---|---|
|   |   | 1 | 2 | 3 | 4 |   |
| 5 | 6 | 7 | 8 | 9 | 10 | 11 |
| 12 | 13 | 14 | 15 | 16 | 17 | 18 |
| 19 | 20 | 21 | 22 | 23 | 24 | 25 |
| 26 | 27 | 28 | 29 | 30 |   |   |

## December

| S | M | T | W | T | F | S |
|---|---|---|---|---|---|---|
|   |   |   |   |   | 1 | 2 |
| 3 | 4 | 5 | 6 | 7 | 8 | 9 |
| 10 | 11 | 12 | 13 | 14 | 15 | 16 |
| 17 | 18 | 19 | 20 | 21 | 22 | 23 |
| 24 | 25 | 26 | 27 | 28 | 29 | 30 |
| 31 |   |   |   |   |   |   |

An Amazon "Top 100" Seller

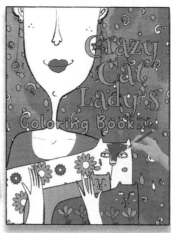

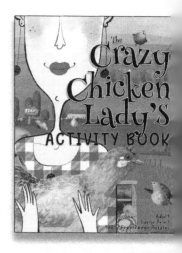

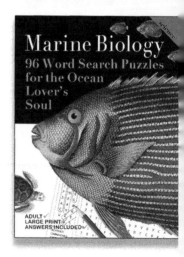

Discover these great books by
Nola Lee Kelsey
www.SoggyNomadPress.com

Don't miss two more great books in
The Ultimate Boondockers Collection!
Enjoy these great dispersed camping-themed
books from Nola Lee Kelsey &
Soggy Nomad Press.

SoggyNomadPress.com

# Help Support a Small Press

## We'll see ya on down the road!

Did you enjoy your 'Ultimate Boondocker's Dispersed Camping Logbook and Journal?' Please tell other campers. Show it to friends, share links on social media and post honest reviews. You'll be helping another nomad grow her small business. It's truly appreciated! Thank you!

- *Nola Lee Kelsey*

Made in the USA
Las Vegas, NV
13 December 2024

13922714R00152